Summer, Sun & Holiday Love

Summer, Sun & Holiday Love

Aus dem Deutschen
von David Fermer

Thienemann

Contents

Sabine Both

Ice-cream With a Kiss

"I can't take this anymore!" says Karolin as she pulls her **'I'm-going-to-collapse' face.** She's been **moaning** next to me on the back seat for ages.

"Just shut up!" I grunt at her.

I can't take it any more either – not after two days in a car which feels like a **pressure cooker**. (Mum is terrified that the smallest gap in the window will let in a highly dangerous **draught** with deadly consequences.) But does that mean I can have a good moan every five minutes? I'm starving! I need a pee! I'm dying of thirst! Little sisters can be such a pain.

In a desperate attempt to try and get an inch of private space within the two square metres of seating, I pull my jacket over my head, despite the fact that it's 45 degrees in the shade in here. Then I shove the walkman earplugs into my ears so hard that it hurts.

What am I doing here? Why am I going all the

'I'm-going-to-collapse' face – „Ich-brech'-gleich-zusammen"-Gesicht; to moan – stöhnen, jammern;
pressure cooker – Dampfkochtopf; draught – Luftzug

way to Sicily instead of being in a dark, cold cave of stalactites far, far away from the holiday-crazed sunglass-wearers? I don't want sun. Why didn't I just stay with Granddad in Bad Neuenahr, with the pensioners and the old **biddies**? Some **mouldy** old granddad would probably have been more than willing to be my holiday flirt.

I hate holiday flirts. Not that I´ve ever had one – apart from the **ankle-biter** in Holland who cooked **jellyfish** pie in a hole in the sand with me at the age of four. But life after a flirt-free holiday gets tougher and tougher from year to year.

Back at school a **gaping chasm** divides the classroom. On the one side, despite the fact that school has already started, the Mediterranean sun continues to shine… over the girls *with* a holiday flirt. They **drivel** over their holiday photos of **wryly** smiling, sun-tanned boys flexing their muscles on the beach. They smear fading **love bites** with oily skin cream to prolong their **shelf life**. They dry each other's tears as – every few minutes – they're gripped by the **agony** of separation. On the other side of the chasm loom ugly, grey clouds… over the girls *without* a holiday flirt. For some strange reason

---

biddie – Oma, Muttchen; mouldy – schimmelig;
ankle-biter – Hosenscheißer; jellyfish – Qualle;
gaping chasm – klaffender Spalt; to drivel – schwätzen;
wryly – schief; love bite – Knutschfleck;
shelf life – Haltbarkeit; agony – Leiden, Qualen

their tans have already faded within the first two lessons. They're busy finishing off their homework, even though none had been set. They offer each other mutual support with their theory that it's far more intellectual and **stands** you **in** better **stead** for the rest of your life to have spent your holiday learning about Greek or Roman culture rather than **smothering** Greek or Roman boys' lips **in** kisses. What **self-deception**!

Why is it that Neckermann & Co. fail to recognise this obvious gap in the market? Why doesn't someone start a Rent-a-Holiday-Flirt agency? Flirts at a daily or weekly rate, affordable even for an average holiday **allowance**. I'd willingly give up a present for a friend or relative if I could bring the facts back home with me instead. Some guy flexing his muscles on the beach. A long-lasting love bite as a bonus prize. When I finish school I could become a millionaire with this innovative idea!

"Hanna, play 'Auntie from Morocco' with me!" Karolin even manages to **drown out** Christina Aguilera's promise in my walkman: *you are beautiful, no matter what they say*!

"Look at that! Palm trees!" squeals Mum, tapping frantically against the window pane. As if the palm trees could hear her!

---

to stand in good stead – zugute kommen;
to smother in – bedecken mit; self-deception – Selbstbetrug;
allowance – Taschengeld; to drown out – übertönen

"Idiot!" roars Dad to top it all.

He's not talking about the palm trees nor my sister or Mum, but some Vespa driver who didn't give way to him. "Stronzo!" shouts Dad right after *idiot,* because it suddenly occurs to him that he's in Italy, and that he always wanted to talk Italian in Italy (if only to justify the **dead-boring** adult education class that he once took).

How do you say *I'm going to* ***puke*** in Italian?

The picture of a nice family. Dad on the left, Mum on the right, and between them my sister and me, walking slowly through the never-ending pedestrian streets of Taormina. The most embarrassing family **stroll**, passing disgusting paper lanterns dangling from tastelessly striped cafe **awnings**, and excessively colourful flower pots on **ramshackle** Italian walls.

"This is just idyllic!" Mum keeps screaming.

Does she always have to shout like that? And what, if you don't mind telling me, is so idyllic about a horde of tourists dressed up to go out? Mums in batik **wrap skirts**, and dads with white socks in greasy suede sandals? And what on earth is idyllic about locals who stare at us as if to say: *keep your mouths shut and spend all your money*!

---

dead-boring – stinklangweilig; to puke – kotzen;
stroll – Spaziergang; awning – Markise;
ramshackle – baufällig; wrap skirt – Wickelrock

I've got the feeling that I'm melting like a piece of cheap chocolate on a heated **dashboard** under my thin pullover. Does this ridiculous paradise also have to be quite so warm at dusk?

"Why didn't you put on something a bit more airy?" asks Mum as she glances suspiciously at the beads of sweat dripping from the sleeves of my pullover. "You've got that lovely new summer dress."

"I'm cold!" I protest. "And you're the only person who thinks that 'lovely' new summer dress is at all lovely!"

I'd rather drown myself in the hotel pool than wander around in that awful summer dress. After all, you don't stuff a walrus into two square centimetres of pink hearts on a light blue background.

"You've got such a lovely figure," murmurs Mum.

Anyone who thinks flowery flip-flops and oversized sea-shell **tiaras** (which make you look like you're in chains) are pretty is obviously foolish enough to also think I'm pretty. And anyway, mothers are blinded and absolutely not **unbiased** when it comes to their own flesh and blood.

In the meantime, we've **wrangled** our way through to the market square. Mum is now gripped by total ecstasy.

---

dashboard – Armaturenbrett; tiara – Diadem;
unbiased – objektiv, unvoreingenommen;
to wrangle – hier: drängeln

"Oh, look at that **fountain**! Let's sit down on the steps and listen to the street musicians!"

Dad and Karolin nod eagerly, and I feel like I'm about to bring up the three-course evening meal onto the historic paving stones. First pasta, then meat, and a dash of tiramisu to finish it off.

"I'm not sitting down at that stupid fountain!" I **scowl**, thrusting my hands grittily onto my hips.

"Why not?" Dad asks mystified. "Are you worried about getting your trousers dirty?"

"**You bet**!" I snarl.

I don't give a damn about my stupid trousers. All I care about is the last, measly crumb of dignity that I can scrape together in the dark depths of my miserable self-esteem! Not even ten horses could drag me onto those steps to voluntarily expose myself to **all and sundry**. For a nightmare has arisen around the fountain – papagallos! Taormina's teenagers stretching as far as the eye can see, casually leaning against their Vespas and coolly running their fingers through their greasy, gelled hair with a cigarette in the corner of their mouth. **Big-headed** machos. Sun-tanned mafiosi. Under no circumstances whatsoever will I sit down amongst this bunch with my *idyllic*-screaming mother, my **bogey-**

---

fountain – Brunnen; to scowl – mürrisch dreinschauen;
You bet – Allerdings!; all and sundry – Hinz und Kunz, Jedermann; big-headed – eingebildet;
bogey-nosed – nasenpopelnd

nosed sister and my guide-book-reading father. I just won't be able to **hack** it.

Dad, Mum and Karolin stroll over to the fountain without taking even the slightest notice of my **gritty defiance**. Fantastic! What now? I can't just stand around here like one of the stupid **marble** statues as if I'd **been stood up** on a date! Maybe I should go back to the hotel alone, crawl into bed and pretend to be suffering from fish poisoning for the rest of the holiday. The only problem is, I haven't eaten fish yet. Nor do I know where the hotel is. Plus I'd have to ask for Dad's permission to go back alone, which means I would have to go over to the fountain... What a hopeless situation.

Dad goes over to the ice-cream parlour and comes back with four huge tubs of ice-cream. Four! One for him, one for Mum, one for Karolin and one for me! And although it's difficult to be sure at this distance, mine looks like it's red. As red as a **raspberry**. A mountain of red raspberry ice-cream. That's not fair! Dad waves the tub at me, and my mouth starts watering **bucket-loads**. Raspberry ice-cream starts arguing with the **Embarrassment** Factor in my head. And, because I'm such a weak-

---

to hack sth – etwas aushalten;
gritty defiance – eiserner Widerstand; marble – Marmor;
to be stood up – sitzen gelassen werden;
raspberry – Himbeere; bucket-loads – literweise;
embarrassment – Peinlichkeit

willed **greedy-guts**, the raspberry ice-cream wins. I can't believe it!

I take a deep breath and try to adopt my best possible '**aloof** pose' (or at least, what I hope looks aloof): eyebrows raised **haughtily**, the corners of my mouth curved downwards **in contempt**. In this pose I **swagger** over to the fountain. The bad thing is, you always get stiff legs when you take on an aloof pose. And it's even worse when those inordinately stiff legs trip you up and you start to stumble.

I stagger, **topple over**, wave my arms around and fall with a loud thump into one of the parked Vespas which goes crashing to the ground. To top it all, the Vespa knocks over its owner as it falls. What an entrance! I land flat on my face in the middle of the Stage of Embarrassment! Then I hear muffled scraps of Italian conversation which seem to be taking place miles away. I'm glad I don't speak Italian! Otherwise I'd now know how to say *fat cow* or *walrus*.

I quickly check that all my body parts are still in one piece, and I **dare** to raise my head. It doesn't take long to realise the state of affairs. The Italian **victim** is lying right next to me. He's as tanned as a sunbed model, his hair is as dark as Black Beauty, and his face is like an Italian version of Leonardo

---

greedy-guts – Vielfraß;
aloof – unnahbar; haughtily – hochmütig;
in contempt – verächtlich; to swagger – stolzieren;
to topple over – umkippen; to dare – wagen; victim – Opfer

DiCaprio. I've managed to pick the most **gorgeous** papagallo in the square! He's obviously managed to survive the incident without losing any of his vital organs either, and he gets to his feet and looks at me with his chocolate-brown eyes.

"Hey, bella!"

Hey, bella? That's not Italian for *walrus* or *fat cow*, that's for sure! As far as my knowledge of Italian goes, *hey* means *hey* and *bella beautiful*. So who's he talking to?

He holds out his hand to me. I take it without thinking, and he pulls me up to my feet. Now he's bound to call me *walrus*. A walrus for which even Italian papagallos need a **hydraulic lift**! But he doesn't say anything. He just gives me a big smile.

"You ... German?" he asks me.

What's that supposed to mean? Is he **taking the mickey**? Is he playing some nasty game with me? Or was that just a statement rather than a question, because every other evening German walruses run into Italian Vespas? Maybe **spotty** German teeny-girls are famous for producing Sicilian **scrap metal**.

I just nod.

"Germania," he says expertly.

I nod again and wait for a word that sounds like

---

gorgeous – umwerfend, atemberaubend;
hydraulic lift – Hebebühne; to take the mickey – sich über jmdn. lustig machen; spotty – pickelig;
scrap metal – Eisen-Schrott

whale. *Whalio* perhaps. Out of the corner of my eye I glance at the Vespa. The wing mirror is broken. Blast! That'll cost me my entire holiday allowance. *Whalio payi payi*. Well, come on, say it!

"Bella ragazza," he says and smiles.

Huh? Pretty girl? He must be suffering from **concussion**. I wait... for everybody who's standing around to burst into laughter. But nobody does. Don't the Italians get irony? It's funny if a whale gets called a *bella ragazza*! I take a look around. White teeth sparkle out of twenty sun-tanned Italian boys' faces. They're smiling. But not **maliciously**, and not disgustedly either. Not even **nonchalantly**, but... well... how can I put it... as if they all wanted a lick of my raspberry ice-cream. Raspberry ice-cream! That's a good **cue**! I pull myself together.

"Er..." I say and point at the Vespa mirror. "Quanta costa?" Was that Italian or Spanish? "What does it cost?" I ask him in English. "How much?" I stutter and rub my fingers together to make sure nothing stands in the way of our understanding.

"Nothing," says the boy, grinning. "Free for the bella ragazza."

He's spent too much time in the sun, that's for sure. But **it suits me**. If I can't save my dignity, then at least I can save my holiday allowance.

---

concussion – Gehirnerschütterung; maliciously – hämisch; nonchalantly – nebensächlich, beiläufig; cue – Stichwort; it suits me – es ist mir recht

"Grazie," I say **succinctly**.

"It's a pleasure," he says.

My hands feel numb, and a hot and cold tickle runs down my spine. I'm completely **out of my depth**. It's worse than all the **National Youth Games** together. I try to twist my mouth into a smile. I think of raspberry ice-cream, turn on the spot, and stagger back towards the fountain, my legs wobbling.

"Well?" laughs Dad. "Already found an admirer?"

I **growl**. Whatever just happened back there must have some rational explanation. There's probably a law here in Taormina which states that every female tourist – no matter what they look like – has to be flirted with in order to support local tourism. Those who fail to do so **face a punishment** of up to three years in prison. The papagallo can probably get a new Vespa mirror free of charge in the town hall. And on top of that he gets a bonus for highly dedicated flirting or for special services to the town of Taormina. Probably all men here aged between 3 and 85 earn a living as professional flirts. Yes, that would explain it! So my presence on this earth today has at least provided an entire Sicilian family with their daily needs. Pasta for all! There are more **superfluous** things to do in this world!

---

succinctly – knapp; to be out of one's depth – überfordert sein; National Youth Games – Bundes-Jugendspiele; to growl – knurren; to face a punishment – mit einer Strafe rechnen; superfluous – überflüssig

The beach! Just the sound of the word squeezes the life out of me. Beach means getting undressed! But not me. I'll be damned if I'm going to present myself to the world in the glaring sun in no more than a **scrap** of clothing.

Mum **haggles** down the rental price of the **sunshades** with the beach-papagallos. How embarrassing! After she's finally finished, we're allowed to take up our post. I squeeze into the only cover between the cooler and Karolin's jumbo blow-up dolphin. That's it. I won't move from the spot for the whole damn day!

Through a gap between the cooler and Mum's huge beach bag I can make out a small section of the beach. There aren't any papagallos as far as the eye can see, but there is a pack of **beach babes** with bum-length, curly brown hair who look like they've been cast for the Italian equivalent of Baywatch. On seeing them I instinctively grab the **bulge of fat** on my stomach. Oh dear! It feels like it's expanded overnight by a few square metres. If I keep stuffing myself with ice-cream and spaghetti, the fat will soon be hanging down from my waist like a waiter's **apron**. Disgusting!

My mood has now sunk so low that not even the Titanic got this deep. I hook up my walkman with

---

scrap – Fetzen; to haggle over sth – um etwas feilschen; sunshade – Sonnenschirm; beach babe – Strandnixe; bulge of fat – Speckwulst; apron – Schürze

my ears and close my eyes once and for all. That is, until I've listened to the whole of the Robbie album and start feeling sick. Not because of Robbie Williams, of course, but because of the overdose of ultra-violet **rays**. My trousers are slowly dissolving and sticking to my **thighs**. My internal organs are boiling like a **casserole**. And in my head the last water particles in my brain seem to be **evaporating**. I have to move. Or at least I have to get out of the blazing sun. I don't have any other choice.

I open my eyes and can't believe what I see. No one's there! My family has disappeared! I look around **bewildered** and spot them in the beach pavilion not too far away sipping at their fruit juices. My bone-dry throat could do with a bit of that. But instead I decide to force down a few sips of the pee-warm sparkling mineral water from an overheated bottle and take over Mum's place under the sunshade. As I crawl towards it on all fours, my path is interrupted by two brown feet. No one in my family has feet as brown as that, that's for sure.

OK, I'm squatting on all fours like a **dumb** dog, and there's nothing I can do now but raise my head. Maybe I'll even bark, just to get it right. I see the brown **calf muscles** with lots of frizzy black hair. Then the brown muscular thighs. After that

---

rays – Strahlen; thighs – Schenkel; casserole – Schmortopf; to evaporate – verdunsten; bewildered – verwirrt; dumb – blöd; calf muscles – Waden

comes a brown stomach with a perfectly shaped belly button and a brown chest with a gold cross on a chain. Well, I'll be damned! I recognise that brown face!

"Hey, bella ragazza! What a great surprise!"

"Hihihi."

How can anyone's giggle sound so stupid? Maybe I really should have barked. I quickly scramble to my feet and try to stand there as **casually** as possible with my legs astride.

"What you do on your own here?"

"Me not alone," I say, my voice regaining its **vigour**, if not its grasp of the English language.

I point towards the beach pavilion without guessing that my entire family is currently looking in our direction, seizing the opportunity to **wave** over to us. I could just die of embarrassment!

"Oh, la famiglia!" he says and I feel like I'm in *The Godfather*. "You at the fountain again tonight?"

I shrug my shoulders.

"I ask your papa if you go with me to drink cappuccino!"

"Are you serious?" The words fall unchecked out of my mouth. It can't be humanly possible that he's serious.

He grins. "You no boyfriend in Germania?" he asks me, **screwing** up his forehead.

---

casually – lässig; vigour – Kraft; to wave – winken;
godfather – Pate; to screw – in Falten legen

"Nope," I say promptly.

"Bravo! Bellissimo!" he calls right across the entire beach.

Just a moment! He's shouting to someone from the local tourist board who is **crouching** somewhere behind a sunshade. He just wants to make sure he gets his flirt bonus again.

"Tell me, do you get money for this?" I ask **viciously**. I've had enough. I'm not going to let him take the mickey out of me any longer.

"For you it don't cost nothing."

He lifts up a box which I hadn't **spotted** until now. A box with a shoulder strap and lots of colourful stickers. Ice-cream. That means he sells ice-cream, I **deduce** quickly, and in the blink of an eye I've got something cold in my hand.

He gives me a smile – ping! – and all of a sudden there are two suns in the sky. Then he turns around and strolls off down the beach. **Paralysed,** I stare at his bottom as it bobs up and down. Even Leonardo couldn't beat that. Not DiCaprio in the flesh, nor old da Vinci with his hammer and **chisel**. He turns around again and smiles. Ping! Now there are four suns in the sky! The beach is glowing as if an invasion of UFOs were sending down intergalactic beams. I stare at him until something cold drips

---

to crouch – hocken; viciously – giftig, boshaft;
to spot – erspähen, erblicken; to deduce – schlussfolgern;
paralysed – gelähmt; chisel – Meißel

onto my foot. The ice-cream in my hand is dissolving into thin air! And at the same time, somewhere inside me the first barricade of the huge, barbed-wire **bulwark** guarding my heart also begins to **melt**.

Karolin comes hopping across the beach towards me, asking me the same question for the hundredth time, "Will you go into the sea with me, Hanna?"

"OK!"

My sister looks at me as if I just said something in Chinese. "OK?"

"Yeah, stop looking so dumb. Why shouldn't I go into the sea with you?"

"Because you never go into the sea with me! You always say that you already know that fat floats on the surface."

It's true. I did use this argument for the last hundred times that Karolin asked me to swim with her, but that was back in the days when the sky was only lit by one single, **pathetic** sun! Now that four suns are orbiting the earth, I've started sweating litres, and unless I get into that sea, I'm going to **burn to a crisp**. And besides, it's about time I rinsed my eyes with saltwater. Maybe then those **bobbing buttocks** will disappear from my **retina**!

---

bulwark – Bollwerk; to melt – schmelzen;
pathetic – erbärmlich; to burn to a crisp – verbrennen, verglühen; bobbing buttocks – wippende Pobacken;
retina – Netzhaut des Auges

I get undressed, wriggle into my bikini under a large towel, strut over the beach like someone who's blessed with astonishing self-confidence (despite the whale shape), and plunge into the cool ocean! Ah, that's good! The pulp in my head slowly begins to re-form into a brain, and I start to think again with a renewed clarity. The first thing I think is: it's pretty unlikely that Taormina gives its teenagers money for flirting with tourists, isn't it?

"What are you doing?"

Karolin is maddening. She grinds her chewing gum with a revolting open mouth and jumps up and down on our shared hotel bed. I'm twisting myself in front of the mirror, trying to catch a glimpse of my back. My back in the new summer dress!

"Gymnastics!" I growl.

"That's a strange kind of gymnastics!"

I sigh and give in. I need her help, whether I want it or not. "Tell me what it looks like from behind."

"Like it always does," she **prattles**.

"The question is, does it make me look fat?!"

"Nope."

"You sure?"

"You're not fat!"

"What's this then?" I pinch the bulge on my thighs.

---

to prattle – plappern

"They're just female curves," says Karolin like a school headmistress.

I can't believe my ears. "Where did you get that from?"

"I heard it."

"Where?"

"Dad told Mum that you're getting female curves now. And Mum said you're in puberty, and that's why you think your female curves are stupid. And Dad said that's why you always think you're too fat, even though you're not fat at all."

I just don't believe it. This **devious** little **brat** picks up everything which is not destined for her ears.

I decide to find a glimmer of truth in Karolin's prattle, and it's the point about me **not actually** being fat. So I keep the summer dress on. In case I really am too fat, I quickly work out how many days of holiday are left in which I will have to traipse around Taormina as the girl who "ridiculously tried to squeeze herself into that far too **skimpy** summer dress." I make it 24. OK. That's the same as an Advent calendar. I'll take the risk.

In a busy street café a tub of ice-cream is propped prominently in front of each member of the family. They're so big it's difficult to see over the top. Mine

---

devious – raffiniert; brat – Gör; not actually – nicht wirklich; skimpy – knapp, luftig

is red! Mum's been staring at me all evening out of the corner of her eye with a stupid grin on her face.

"What?" I ask at last, as **irritated** as hell.

"Oh, nothing. I'm just happy you've finally put on your summer dress. It really suits you."

Maddening, that's what it is. I can already imagine Mum and Dad lying in bed tonight, grinning at each other while they discuss my hormonal condition. *Now she's wearing dresses. That means she'll soon be getting her period. Which means acne can't be far off. Which means we'll slowly have to resign ourselves to the fact that we're going to be grandparents soon.* Don't I have a life of my own? Do parents always have to know everything that's going on? And do they always have to know it before you've found it out for yourself? And do they have to…

"Evening, me don't want to disturb the famiglia, but me want to introduce myself. Fabio Arrizzi!"

The ice-cream boy! I instinctively move my shoulders forward, arch my back and **anxiously** try to stretch the far too short dress over my thighs.

Fabio Arrizzi shakes everybody's hand. Even Karolin's. But not mine. He just grins at me wryly. Ping! It's pitch black. What are the four suns doing in the ice-cream parlour at this time of night?

"Me want to ask if I take your daughter for cappuccino."

---

irritated – entnervt; to resign – sich abfinden;
anxiously – ängstlich

Dad and Mum glance at each other hesitantly. It's the first time they've ever been asked officially for a date with their little daughter. Please, please be cool, dear parents! Don't even start thinking about all the terrible things that could go wrong. Just see it for what it is: a cappuccino for your little daughter, who hates coffee like **heartburn**, but whose greatest wish right now is to run off with the ice-cream boy in her far-too-short dress. Dear parents, if you really are fully informed about my physical condition, then you shouldn't have too much difficulty deducing my emotional state of mind! But then again... My emotional state of mind suddenly begins to **waver**. Do I even want to go with him for a cappuccino? Wouldn't I far prefer to dress and undress Karolin's Barbie with her in our hotel room?

Help!

"Do you want to go?" asks Dad in my direction.

I nod as if I were trying to shake my head off. I don't actually want to, but I want to!

"OK then. We can meet up in an hour at the fountain," says Mum.

All I can think as I pour the disgusting brown brew into my mouth is that it tastes like a freshly asphalted road. The question is: What can I say?

"**Yum!**"

---

heartburn – Sodbrennen; to waver – wanken; yum – lecker

"Oh, it good taste, bella ragazza."

"Hanna," I suggest.

"Hanna. Beautiful name."

He smiles, and all of a sudden the cappuccino tastes really quite good. Something about the way Fabio looks at me manages to attack my protective wall again. This time he goes for the **concrete** barricade with the steel **reinforcements**. I'm melting!

"You know something crazy? At first I thought you probably got money for talking to me."

Oh no! Is that what happens when I give my heart a bit of freedom? If that's the case, then I should obviously ask for a gang of builders to erect a double-thick mega-wall **on the spot**! How could I say something like that?

Fabio looks bewildered. Then he laughs. "I think your father prefer to give money so he don't have to talk to you. He looked at me like a **squid** looks at its food in sea."

I have to laugh. In doing so I **splutter** a mouthful of cappuccino over the table. Well done!

"And you just like your papa. A little squid spitting ink!"

He slaps his thigh and laughs so loud that tears start rolling down his brown cheeks. And I just have to laugh with him. I forget that my **joints** are

---

concrete – Beton; reinforcement – Verstärkung;
on the spot – auf der Stelle; squid – Tintenfisch;
to splutter – prusten; joints – Gelenke

as stiff as **celery**. The knot in my throat seems to evaporate into thin air. I feel like a child, who's just spent hours playing outside, slipping into a hot bathtub, exhausted and as happy as can be.

"Come with me," he says suddenly, **tossing** some money onto the table. He takes my hand and pulls me up from my chair.

I follow him across the busy street into a side alley and up two sets of **crooked** steps. There's no one around – even the voices and tooting Vespas fade away into the distance – but I'm not scared in the least.

We walk across a small square up to a balustrade and, all of a sudden, I have a breathtaking view of the sea crashing against the rocks fifty metres below. Everything is bathed in the silver moonlight. On the **shoreline** to our left and right a few lights are on in the houses. A small black cat runs across the balustrade. It's **stunningly** beautiful.

"Here is away from many people," says Fabio looking dreamily into the distance. "I like this place."

"Me, too," I say.

"Are you feeling sick?" asks Karolin as she piles the seventh portion of scrambled egg from the breakfast buffet onto her plate.

---

celery – Sellerie; to toss – werfen; crooked – windschief; shoreline – Ufer, Küstenlinie; stunning – atemberaubend

"No. I feel on top of the world," I say from the bottom of my heart.

"You keep **groaning** as if you were sick."

"I'm not groaning, I'm sighing," I explain.

"Because of Fabio," concludes Karolin expertly. "When you were with him yesterday, Mum and Dad said that you're coming into that age now, and Dad said he needed another ice-cream to get over the shock."

"What is it you actually do to make everybody think you're *not* **eavesdropping**?" I ask Karolin with a shake of my head.

"I pick my nose and look like I'm **not all there**," she says as if it were the most obvious thing in the world.

My sister! Every day she runs past me thousands of times, and I've never even noticed that, behind those **chubby cheeks** of hers, there lies a really smart little person. I suppose it's quite good actually. Maybe she's finally old enough to talk to about the important things in life.

"Do you know what?" I say without delay. "I think I'm in love."

Karolin looks at me and shakes her head as if I were the picture of hopeless stupidity. "Oh, Hanna, everybody knows that anyway!"

We go back to the table. We've only just sat down

---

to groan – stöhnen; to be eavesdropping – lauschen;
not all there – nicht ganz da; chubby cheeks – Pausbacken

when the breakfast waiter comes over to us and starts clearing away the dirty dishes. In doing so he drops something into my lap.

"What... er...?"

Why did the breakfast waiter just **kick my ankle**? Disgraceful! He can't just... just a moment! The waiter pulls a face as if he were going to skin me alive. He's trying to let me know something. The penny slowly drops: perhaps he dropped something onto my lap **on purpose**. I instinctively pick up the folded piece of paper. The waiter's face relaxes. He smiles.

Karolin rolls her eyes. She doesn't miss a thing. I put my finger up to my lips and glare at her to make sure she knows that if she tells anyone one word about this, it would mean instant death.

"So, off we go then," trumpets Dad as he wipes the remaining jam from the corner of his mouth. "Go and get your sunhats. We're taking a tour today."

I haven't got any time **to get worked up about** the fact that we're going to spend the whole day in the burning heat, running over **red-hot piles of stones**. I dart to my hotel room as if a tarantula had just bitten me and unfold the piece of paper. What

---

to kick one's ankle – jmdn. ans Bein treten;
on purpose – mit Absicht;
to get worked up about sth – sich über etwas aufregen;
red-hot piles of stones – heiß glühende Steinhaufen

on earth does the hotel waiter want to write to me about?

Ciao, Hanna, your waiter is my cousin. Don't worry. I no sell ice today on beach. I go with my uncle to Palermo. Do we see us in evening? I want. *Fabio*

Whoa! I get a rush of adrenaline like when I play the piano to an audience. My entire breakfast is **digested** within a few seconds and is knocking to come out. But I don't have any time to go to the toilet. I grab my notebook and quickly write a reply.

Ciao, Fabio. I'm not on the beach today either. Today is culture day. Looking forward to this evening. I'll keep an eye out for you. *Hanna*

I rush back to the breakfast room and give the piece of paper to Fabio's cousin. Now Dad can drag me through as much **rubble** as he wants. I'll just let everything go over my head with an **elated** smile.

Dear Diary!
Tours, day-trips, shopping. Nothing gets on my nerves anymore. I even sometimes catch myself squealing the word "idyllic". Just as well no one knows me here. I just patiently let all that culture go over my head and think

---

to digest – verdauen; rubble – Trümmer; elated – beseelt

about meeting Fabio every evening. It's so cool. We get on better from evening to evening. We wander through Taormina's alleyways and tell each other jokes which we both laugh at – even if we don't get the punchline. Sometimes Fabio says such sweet things in his funny English. The time with him always flies by. By the time we look at our watch, an hour has already passed. Then we quickly run over to our favourite spot and end the evening at the balustrade, looking out over the sea while holding hands. I can't even begin to describe how I feel at that moment. Like candy floss. Or like I'm completely drunk. I'm so terribly happy and utterly in love!

Karolin has crept up from behind and is trying to catch a glimpse into my diary. I slam it shut in front of her nose. "What do you want?"

Karolin puts on an important expression.

"What?" I growl.

"Yesterday Dad said to Mum that he doesn't like you going off like you do every evening."

Oh-oh. That doesn't sound good.

"And what did Mum say to that?" I ask anxiously.

Karolin points at the diary. No more information for free! But maybe there's a law that permits you to **strangle** younger sisters? In self-defence! Or for **unreasonable** emotional cruelty?

I surrender. I open the diary and let Karolin read

---

punchline – Pointe; candy floss – Zuckerwatte;
to strangle – erwürgen; unreasonable – unzumutbar

the last entry. She reads and reads and reads. Her lips mouth letter after letter, and she grunts with satisfaction after deciphering each and every word. This will take years!

I get a bit panicky. "Come on, tell me what Mum said."

"There's never anything interesting in your stupid diary. Just this falling in love rubbish."

This child is killing me!

"What did Mum say? Spit it out, or I'll make sure your blow-up dolphin runs out of air once and for all!"

Now it's Karolin's turn to panic. "Mum said not to forget that it's a holiday, and Dad said that's right, he wants to spend the evenings of his holiday with all his family together, nice and **cosy**."

"Oh shit!"

"What? Again?" Dad pulls an upset face and looks over his tub of ice-cream from me to Fabio and from Fabio to Mum.

Damn! I was hoping that a whole day full of ancient ruins and incredibly long lectures by dead-boring tourist guides would have put him in such a good mood that he wouldn't even consider ruining my holiday! Not a chance! I send a quick prayer to heaven. Please help Dad **act out of character**.

---

cosy – gemütlich;
to act out of character – über den eigenen Schatten springen

"Let her go," says Mum.

Very helpful. Can't she make a **fiery speech** to make it perfectly clear to him that my **spiritual welfare** is at stake here? That – with a wrong decision – he could decide on the long-term development of my life? That I'd be a psychological wreck if he now starts to **play up** and get selfish? Doesn't anyone here understand that this isn't about some date, but that my heart's been driving me crazy all day and can only be saved from complete collapse through one whole hour together with Fabio? Can't anybody just do something?!

"If you don't mind, I like to sit with you." Fabio smiles – melting the ice-cream in the tubs.

Dad opens his mouth and closes it. I'm screaming for joy inside. Now Dad just can't say no. That would be far too **impolite**. "Please, take a seat," says Dad, pulling up a chair for Fabio.

I feel something under the table touching my knee. Fabio's hand. I quickly put my hand in his and squeeze it tight. Well done!

And Fabio goes from good to better. He wraps Dad around his little finger like a **piece of string**.

"Yes, there be many **excavations** in Sicily. It be cultural very interesting place."

---

fiery speech – flammende Rede;
spiritual welfare – Seelenheil; to play up – Theater machen;
impolite – unhöflich; piece of string – ein Stück Schnur;
excavations – Ausgrabungen

Bravo! Dad catches on fire and starts **talking shop** with Fabio about crumbling **columns**, while I soothe my **wriggling** heart under the table in Fabio's hand. As if in a petrol station I draw life-saving energy from this warm, soft hand and recharge my batteries. I creep into the palm of his hand with the whole of my body, like a cuckoo into its nest, and dream of the small square near the balustrade, and of how it feels when Fabio puts his arm around my waist as we look out over the sea together. I dream of how it is when Fabio plucks a **strand** of hair out of my face, looks deep into my eyes and that moment comes when I can't decide which is bigger: the sea or Fabio's eyes.

"You live in a country that has a lot of history," says Dad and I emerge from my dreams.

"Si," answers Fabio. "Tomorrow I no work selling ice-cream on beach. It possible for me to make trip on Vespa with Hanna to temple not far from here?"

"Of course!" says Dad, grinning **delighted**.

Fabio is simply phenomenal! He's even managed to make Dad forget that Vespas are those things on which his daughter is simply not allowed to sit, because they always drive into **brick walls**. Life can be so wonderful!

---

to talk shop – fachsimpeln; column – Säule; to wriggle – zappeln; strand – Strähne; delighted – erfreut, zufrieden; brick walls – Steinmauern, Hauswände

The countryside flies past. I feel the wind in my hair. The road races by under my bum. My arms are wrapped around Fabio's waist. If this isn't heaven on earth, what is?!

Fabio stretches out his hand and points to a few crooked columns propped up between **withered** olive trees which **swelter** in the midday heat. We've arrived.

Fabio takes me by the hand and leads me through knee-high grass towards the temple. We come across a small spot of shade under a tree and take shelter under it.

Fabio has thought of everything. He'd taken a bag from the Vespa's carrier and, with a few **flicks of the wrist**, he's spread out a picnic in front of us. Water melon. **Peaches**. Bread and salami. A big bottle of 7-Up. Our mouths sink into the dripping pieces of melon, and we **have a race** to spit out the **pips** into the grass. Then we lie back, listen to the grasshoppers chirping, and hold hands.

"Tell me," I begin, "do you actually think I'm pretty?"

Fabio sits up and looks at me with his chocolate brown eyes. They look like they could start melting and dripping out of his face any second. "What you ask?" he says. "You no pretty. You beautiful."

---

withered – verdorrt; to swelter – brüten;
flicks of the wrist – Handgriffe; peach – Pfirsich;
to have a race – etwas um die Wette tun; pips – Kerne

"Really?"

"Si. You bellissima." Fabio takes my hand and pulls me up. Then he looks at me from head to foot. "You know what I see?"

I shake my head.

"I see hair, colour of vanilla ice-cream, feels like **silk**. I see eyes, colour of sea, big and round, like a whole world in there. And then I see beautiful... How you say?" He runs his hands over my shoulders.

"Shoulders," I say.

"Beautiful shoulders." He laughs. "Like hills in **Tuscany**. And then I see a body like Venus, with legs so long like bella Italia on the map."

Now I can't help bursting into laughter.

"And then I see laughter. And laughter is like sun."

"And when you laugh, there are always four suns in the sky," I say.

Fabio stops laughing all of a sudden. He looks at me seriously. So seriously that my head suddenly starts to **spin**. Blast! I can feel that something really momentous is about to happen. And this momentous event has something to do with my lips which are **sizzling** as if I'd just swallowed an overdose of **sherbet**. Oh-oh. I'm about to be kissed! The first kiss in my life!

Fabio pulls me close to him. Then he lowers his

---

silk – Seide; Tuscany – Toskana; to spin – sich drehen;
to sizzle – kribbeln; sherbet – Brausepulver

head to mine. I close my eyes. Thanks to the effects of excessive adrenalin, my eyes are **blurred** anyway. I brace my lips. I have to make some contribution of my own to the situation. I'm dying with **suspense**. For a moment I think how nice it would be to be lying in the sun right now, sucking nonchalantly on a straw. I'm not ready yet! But I have to be ready! There's no turning back. My mouth is about to be **deflowered**...

Something rubs against my nose. I open my eyes in irritation. Am I hallucinating? No, I'm not! Fabio is rubbing his nose against mine. The vibration alarm suddenly switches off in my lips, and my brain sends an all-clear to all my body cells: kiss **postponed** to uncertain date! Please relax!

Rubbing noses is nice. I turn my head from one side to the other and rub my nose over Fabio's cheeks. The little hairs in his face tickle, and I breathe in the smell of his skin deeply. It smells wonderful. Like raspberry ice-cream. Only better.

Dear Diary!
We rub our noses together a lot. And we rub our noses against our ears. And we stroke each other. On the back. On the arms. Even on the stomach. But we haven't kissed. I think neither of us dare. And I have absolutely no idea how kissing is ever going to actually happen.

---

blurred – verschwommen; suspense – Spannung;
to deflower – entjungfern; to postpone – verschieben

"You still haven't kissed?" Karolin has successfully **crept up** from behind and read everything over my shoulder.

I slam the diary shut, **incensed**. The little monster!

"No, not yet. Even though it's got nothing to do with you."

Karolin pulls a **nauseated** face. "Ohhh! You **scaredy-cats**! When I'm as old as you I'll be kissing from dawn to dusk."

"Sure you will: Auntie Käthi on her wet lips for Christmas."

This little rat talks about things she's got as much idea about as I do about integral arithmetic. In other words, nothing!

"It's not that difficult!" Karolin continues to babble, rolling onto her blow-up dolphin and kissing his rubber nose like some insane **sledge-hammer**.

"Yeah, right. Really easy!" I laugh at her. "Don't you know that when you kiss you're meant to open your mouth and use your tongue?"

Bulls-eye!

Karolin stares at me as if I'd just claimed the earth was flat.

"What a load of rubbish!" she says, quite sure of

---

to creep up – sich anschleichen; incensed – empört; nauseated – angewidert; scaredy-cats – Feiglinge; sledge-hammer – Vorschlaghammer; bulls-eye – Treffer!

herself. "Nobody does that. That would be totally **weird.**"

"Oh yeah? I thought you knew all about kissing."

She doesn't **know if she's coming or going**!

"Mum!!"

Oh no, I should have kept my big mouth shut! Karolin starts **bawling** across the whole beach, and Mum immediately comes running over.

"What happened?" she asks nervously.

She's probably worried that Karolin has lodged a **sea-urchin** in her foot! Boy, she deserves to!

"Mum, Hanna is so disgusting! She says that when people kiss they put their tongue into each other's mouth! That's not true, is it?"

Mum's face clearly betrays what she's thinking: why didn't I just fail to hear the screams of my second born? I'm on holiday. Why do I have to **put up with** such complicated things?

I grin. I really want to see how Mum wriggles her way out of this one.

"Yes, well…" she begins.

So far, so good.

"…in principle… well, generally speaking… let me put it like this: there are different ways of kiss-

---

weird – schräg, abartig;
to know not, if one's coming or going – völlig verunsichert sein; to bawl – plärren; sea-urchin – Seeigel;
to put up with sth – sich mit etwas herumschlagen

ing. One way, for instance, is kissing someone on the cheek..."

Yawn!

"...another way is to kiss someone on the lips..."

And the birds and the bees?

"...Yes, and the third way, that's the way men and women kiss when they love each other and... well, when they do *that,* they occasionally do it with their tongues."

"That's soooo disgusting!" Karolin wipes her mouth with the back of her hand as if she'd just been given a tonguey kiss by Dieter Bohlen.

"You and Dad, do you do it, too?" she shrieks, shuddering at the thought.

"Er. We do," says Mum **warily**.

Karolin now completely loses it. She shakes herself as if she were trying to shake off her own skin. Hopping from one foot to the other, she runs over to the sea screaming loudly, where she starts wildly beating the innocent surface of the water with her arms.

I shake my head **magnanimously**. Mum looks like she's seriously questioning my sister's mental health.

"Why did you tell her?" she asks.

"Because she gets on my nerves!"

Mum shrugs her shoulders. "Well, she'll just

---

to yawn – gähnen; warily – vorsichtig, behutsam; magnanimously – nachsichtig have to put up with it. It won't be the last time." Then she looks at me inquisitively out of the corner of her eyes. "Well?"

"Well what?"

"Are you only an expert in theory or in practice as well?"

She's got me there! I shrug my shoulders and shift the sand around at my feet from left to right.

Mum puts her arm around my shoulders and puts on her most **thoughtful** face. "Tonight's your last chance, isn't it?"

That hit the mark, too! Mum really has a nasty habit of rubbing your nose right into the harsh reality. Until now I'd been doing really well at **avoiding** this fact. Until now I was a master of being in the Here and Now.

And Mum destroys all my fragile castles in the air with one sentence: "You know... tomorrow we're going home."

Something wet starts to build up ominously in the corner of my eye. A **lump** the size of a tennis ball begins to block up my throat. **It's desperate** to break free in the form of a big sob. I jump up and run after my sister into the sea. I'd really like to beat the water like crazy with my arms as well, but I'm definitely too old for that. So I just dive into the

---

thoughtful – verständnisvoll;
to avoid – aus dem Weg gehen, vermeiden; lump – Kloß;
to be desperate – etwas dringend wollen

water and swim to the bottom where no one can hear me when I scream.

Ahhhhhhhhhh!

Mum on the left, Dad on the right, in between Karolin and me. That's how we stroll through Taormina's most beautiful street for the last time. It's like the last meal before an **execution**. Everything around me makes the lump in my throat swell up even more, and my eyes are a constantly **moist biotope**. I have the feeling the sky is sparkling with stars even more than ever before. The air is milder and sweeter. The **snatches of Italian** sound more wonderful. The paper lanterns hanging down from the stripped café awnings are more colourful. The **teeming** flower pots on the old Italian walls are **lusher** than before. I'd really like go down on my hands and knees and kiss the **cobbled ground** like the **Pope**. I want to cling on to the edge of the fountain and become one of the water-spewing figures, just so that I never have to leave this place. I run my hand over the surface of the ice-cream parlour table and stare at the menu until I have it imprinted photographically on my memory. An extra-large portion of raspberry ice-cream

---

execution – Hinrichtung; moist biotope – Feuchtbiotop;
snatches of Italian – italienische Sprachfetzen;
to teem – überquellen; lush – üppig;
cobbled ground – Kopfsteinpflaster; Pope – Papst

for the last time. I will never eat such fantastic raspberry ice-cream ever again in my life. I'm quite sure of that.

I stare into the mountain of red, but feel too weak to hold my spoon, despite the fact that my stomach has **denied** itself any form of **nutrition** since breakfast.

"Now come on, eat something," says Dad. He's completely out of his depth with my **gloomy** sadness. "When we get home, I'll buy that thing you've wanted to have for months."

That *thing* is a kickboard. And I haven't wanted it for months, I've wanted it for years. But now I don't want it anymore. There's only one thing I really want, and that's to stay here. With Fabio.

"Ciao."

Telepathy. Fabio is standing in front of our table. He pulls up a chair and drops into it like a wet sack.

I immediately grab his hand. He squeezes mine as if he wanted to make apple sauce out of it.

"Ciao," trumpets Dad. "How are you?"

Fabio sighs deeply.

Dad turns desperately to Mum, as if to say "do something!"

"I think the two of them would like to say goodbye to each other alone," says Mum.

I give Mum a look that could melt the whole of the North Pole.

---

to deny – verweigern; nutrition – Nahrung; gloomy – düster

Mum smiles at me. "And I think they should have enough time to do so. So this evening, as an **exception**, two hours. Fabio, please bring Hanna to the hotel at ten o'clock, OK?"

Fabio smiles from ear to ear. I smile from ear to ear as well. Dad looks **hesitant**, but I don't give him any time to think. I just pull Fabio up from his chair and **drag** him out of Dad's reach **without delay**.

We both know where we want to go. Our square! Once over the busy street, down the side alley, up the two sets of crooked steps, right across the small square to the balustrade.

Fabio stands behind me and wraps his arms around my waist. We look out over the sea and the lump in my throat is about the size of an overripe water melon. There's no way I can swallow. I just stand there and **choke**. And then I can't hold it back any more. Tears start rolling down my cheeks, **no holds barred**.

Fabio turns to me. "Bella ragazza," he whispers.

He can't think of anything else to say. He pulls me to him and strokes my back. I press my head to his shoulder and wrap my arms around his neck. I'll just have to eat him up so that he can stay with me forever! In fact, I'll do exactly that. I'll **gobble** him **up**, skin and hair and all! My mouth starts

---

exception – Ausnahme; hesitant – zögerlich; to drag – zerren; without delay – unverzüglich, sofort; to choke – würgen; no holds barred – ungebremst; to gobble up – verschlingen

moving of its own accord. My lips kiss his neck, kiss his chin, kiss his nose, kiss his cheeks.

"Hanna," he whispers. Then he takes my face in his hands and smiles.

I'm not at all nervous. In fact, I'm completely calm. I'm finally ready! And then he kisses me.

For a whole two hours.

"How can anyone double their baggage in only two weeks?" grumbles Dad as he **irritably** tries to squeeze the amphorae, the terracotta masks and the **busts** of gods into the **boot** of the car.

I stare down the street as if turned to stone, even though I know perfectly well that there's no point. Fabio can't come. He went to the **mainland** with his uncle early this morning. My heart is as heavy as a bowling ball. I run my fingers over my lips, and a **tingle** goes down my spine as I think about Fabio's goodbye kiss.

"I saw you!" Karolin lets the air out of her blow-up dolphin and looks at me **boldly**.

"No, you didn't!" I grunt at her. "You were already asleep in bed."

"Oh yes, I did! I saw everything!"

I look **furtively** at the hotel façade. Sure enough, our hotel room has a clear view of the street. And

---

irritably – genervt; bust – Büste; boot – Kofferraum; mainland – Festland; tingle – Kribbeln, prickeln; boldly – frech, herausfordernd; furtively – verstohlen

Fabio and I said our last farewells under the spotlight of the street lamp.

"So what did you see?" I ask Karolin, clinging on to the hope that she's lying.

"First you came up arm in arm. Then you both stood underneath the street lamp. And then you kissed each other for ages. I couldn't tell if it was with or without tongues, even though I would like to have seen what it looks like..."

Karolin had obviously **swallowed** the story with the tongues, and instead of **revolting** her, she was now interested in **getting to the bottom** of it.

"...you hugged each other, like when you try to squeeze the last bit of toothpaste out of the toothpaste tube, and you made really stupid faces as if you were both feeling sick. Then you ran back to the hotel as fast as you could. But when I was just about to go to bed, you came running back, and the kissing thing started all over again. And the hugging. And then you ran off again. And ran back. And that happened at least five times." Karolin **smirks** from one ear to the other. She didn't miss a thing. "And when you finally came back to the room, I pretended I was asleep, and you cried your eyes out. I really wanted to sleep, but I couldn't

---

to swallow – schlucken; to revolt – sich ekeln;
to get to the bottom of sth – einer Sache auf den Grund gehen; to smirk – grinsen

because you kept on crying. It was really annoying."

Karolin's blow-up dolphin is as flat as a pancake, and she folds him up **meticulously**. "I tell you, I'm not going to fall in love when I'm older," she says busily. "It's worse than **toothache, vomiting and diarrhoea** all at the same time."

She's right. I haven't felt this bad all my life.

"Everything in. Right, off we go!" Dad slams the boot shut and **shoos** us into the car. In front of us lie a thousand kilometres in a boiling hot oven.

Karolin and I kneel down on the back seat and watch the hotel through the rear window. Dad drives around the corner. The hotel gradually gets narrower and then disappears. I fall back onto the seat and fight back the tears.

"Look!" shouts Karolin, slapping me on my shoulder.

I jump back onto my knees. In the distance someone is running towards our car and waving as if he'd been bitten by a tarantula. Fabio!

"Dad!!!" I scream. "Stop the car! Stooooop!!"

Dad panics and **slams on the brakes**. "Why? What happened? Where?" he stutters.

I don't have any time for explanations. I jump out

---

meticulously – sorgfältig; toothache – Zahnweh;
vomiting and diarrhoea – Brechdurchfall;
to shoo – scheuchen;
to slam on the brakes – auf die Bremsen steigen

of the car and run towards Fabio and throw myself into his arms. He's completely out of breath.

"I... wanted..." he mumbles. He doesn't know what to say.

For a moment we look at each other sadly in the eyes. Then Fabio smiles. And – ping! – suddenly three additional suns light up the sky.

"See you this evening," he says.

"Yes, this evening... in the ice-cream parlour," I say and run back to the car.

"Did you take a photo of him?" asks Mum as we wait in the long **queue** of cars to get onto the **ferry**.

Damn it! I don't have one! I don't even have one single photo of Fabio! And I don't even have a love bite. I have no **proof**!

I can't help smiling. Who cares? When I get back to school there'll be not one, but – ping! – four Mediterranean suns shining over me.

"No, I don't need a photo," I say. "I'll never forget him anyway."

---

queue – Schlange; ferry – Fähre; proof – Beweis

Thomas Brinx/Anja Kömmerling

The Traffic Jam Prince

Every summer when we go on holiday it's absolute chaos. We all go together: my dad, whose nerves are most **fragile;** my mum, who brings Tom and Jerry along, the two canaries who **refuse** to sing; Grandma Hilde, previously known as **Hot** Hilde, who brings along her poodle Nightlife (which is what she misses); and my **randy** elder sister, Hella, who only thinks of boys, boys, boys and nothing else. She was born with MP3-player headphones in her ears. Since then they've grown, and now it's impossible for her to remove them. Ever. This explains why she has to talk so loudly, and why – theoretically – everybody else should plug up their ears with MP3-player headphones just to make her **bearable**.

We always go to Austria by car. We don't have enough money to go any further, or enough for a new car. So the prehistoric Passat just has to do the job. We all **squeeze** into it, but it's really no prob-

---

fragile – zerbrechlich, empfindlich; to refuse – sich weigern; hot – hier: wild; randy – geil; bearable – erträglich; to squeeze – quetschen

lem at all, because – even though we have enough luggage to fill a minibus (at least) – we only have to drive eight hours.

"Why should we let those **vultures** in the service areas get their **grubby** hands on our money?" Dad has a habit of saying.

Why indeed? Because Mum and Grandma Hilde have enough boiled eggs, cut sandwiches and chilled drinks for at least four coolers. Fruit, vegetables, herring, everything.

But despite all this, we still have to keep making stops on the motorway, because Nightlife has got a **minuscule bladder**, according to Grandma Hilde (though she always pops to the toilet at the same time herself – just to be on the safe side).

And this year everything is the same as always.

"No **traffic jams** on the motorway!" **claims** the radio traffic service.

Mum **anxiously** hangs up a towel to block out the light coming through the right-hand car window. Tom and Jerry can't take the heat. Dad curses as he tries to **cram** the luggage into the **boot** and slam it shut – an act of near impossibility – and in the end he just ties the boot down with a **rope**. Hella sits down on the right-hand side of the back

---

vulture – Geier; grubby – schmuddelig;
minuscule bladder – winzige Blase; traffic jam – Stau;
to claim – verkünden, behaupten; anxiously – ängstlich;
to cram – stopfen; boot – hier: Kofferraum; rope – Seil

seat, **singing** noisily and **out of key** to whatever is coming out of her implanted headphones. Grandma Hilde drops herself down in the middle with Nightlife and, as the engine starts, the poodle immediately starts to imitate Hella – the only difference being he's **howling** because he hates driving. But that's all no problem either, because we'll only be on the road for eight hours. I squeeze myself into the remaining space on the left-hand side of the back seat, and Dad shuts the door from the outside. At last we're ready to go.

Dad has to find the way all on its own, because there's no chance of Mum checking a road atlas. The big cage, with Tom and Jerry inside, is **perched** on her lap, and because it's so dark (the windows are all covered), I need a **torch** to read my book.

"I was never able to read in the car," recalls Grandma Hilde as ever. "I once tried, but I uuurrgghh-ed straight away. Know what I mean?!"

Does it make the picture I have in my head less disgusting just because Grandma Hilde didn't say the word? Hella tears down the towel from her window so that she can look out.

"Hella, think of Tom and Jerry!" **shrieks** Mum, but Hella just ignores her. "Heeellaaa!" Then she gives up, because Dad beeps the **horn**.

---

to sing out of key – falsch singen; to howl – heulen, jaulen;
to perch – thronen; torch – Taschenlampe;
to shriek – kreischen; horn – Hupe

"Every year the same **crap**!" he curses.

Then my parents start **arguing**, because Mum doesn't want Dad to use such bad language when I'm around. Hot Hilde doesn't know what the **fuss** is about. 'Uuurrgghh' is a perfectly normal word. Nightlife starts howling again, and I have absolutely no desire to take part in a discussion about whether fourteen-year-old girls should have to hear the word "crap" or not. There are times when I just wish I had Hella's implanted headphones.

"Wow, what a **cute** guy!" squeals Hella all of a sudden. "Look, Sophie!"

Hella makes a hobby of spotting cute guys wherever she looks, but usually it's not worth looking at them at all. As always, I **peep** past Grandma Hilde and look out of Hella's window. Someone is overtaking us on the right. *First mistake*. It's a dark BMW and much faster than us. *Second mistake*. On the back seat is an unbelievably cute looking guy who blows a huge bubble with his chewing gum. *No mistake*.

Dad flips out. "That's just typical. But I tell you, he won't get there any quicker. And to overtake on the inside! On the inside! I'll **report** him to the police, the big shot. Does he think he's the hero of the underworld just because he's got a **posh** car, or what?"

---

crap – Scheiße; to argue – streiten; the fuss – das Theater; cute – süß; to peep – spähen; to report – hier: anzeigen; posh – edel, schnieke

"Robert!" warns Mum, because she hates it when Dad **gets** all **worked up**. But he doesn't even hear her, because he's attached his hand permanently to the horn.

"Not bad at all, that guy!" whispers Grandma Hilde, and all three of us stare over to the BMW where the bubble gum bursts all over the really **gorgeous** face of – well, let's just call him Bubbles. He starts to peel the sticky gum off his face, and he looks over to us **embarrassed**. His father is beeping his horn back at my Dad and giving it all he's got in the **swearing** department.

"Open the window, Mathilde!" Dad shouts at Mum.

She wraps her arms around the bird cage, purses her lips and shakes her head. "Not on your life!"

Bubbles' Dad overtakes us with ease. Bubbles waves goodbye to us for a split second. We raise our hands back – Hella, Grandma Hilde and I – and then he's gone.

"What a **disgrace**!" shouts Hella. "Such a **magnificent specimen** just slips through my fingers!"

"I'll catch up with him, just you wait," **growls** Dad.

The **exhaust pipe** goes bang, and Grandma Hilde starts telling some story from the days when she

---

to get worked up – sich aufregen; gorgeous – umwerfend, atemberaubend; embarrassed – verlegen; to swear – fluchen; disgrace – Schande; magnificent specimen – Prachtexemplar; to growl – knurren; exhaust pipe – Auspuff

was still known as Hot Hilde. "Back then, when I was a bit **steadier on my feet**, I would have torn off my clothes and run after him – on my own feet – as it were. Once I even...!"

"Oh, don't start all that, Mummy! No one believes you anyway," **whinges** Mum as she blows a kiss to Tom and Jerry.

Grandma Hilde shrugs her shoulders.

She doesn't care in the least if we believe her or not. But Hella's now so worked up she's literally **dying to** get out of the car and tear her clothes off. I stare out of my window as if it wasn't covered with a towel (meaning: I stare at Mum's best kitchen towel) and think about Bubbles. How nice, him waving at us like that!

"He said goodbye to me in such a nice way," squeals Hella.

Actually I had a **sneaking** feeling he'd waved at me, but if that's how Hella sees it, she's probably right. She knows about men.

"When men wave!" sighs Grandma Hilde, stroking Nightlife's hairy head. "Do you **need a pee**, darling?"

Dad collapses onto the steering wheel with a **groan**. "Nightlife needs a pee!"

---

to be steady on the feet – gut zu Fuß sein;
to whinge – meckern, nörgeln; to die to – etwas unbedingt wollen; sneaking – heimlich; to need a pee – pinkeln müssen; groan – Stöhnen

Although, **supposedly,** we never stop at service areas and never spend even a penny there, in fact, we always manage to stop and blow our money in them. Grandma runs to the toilet with Nightlife (we all know who really needs a pee). Mum walks up and down the tiny strip of grass so that Tom and Jerry can get some fresh air in the desperate hope that they will start to sing. My sister Hella spots some complete strangers – some biker guys – and saunters up to them casually, and in utter frustration Dad decides to **vacuum clean** the car, because he had to stop even though he didn't need any petrol.

I go into the shop and buy everything that isn't already in Mum and Grandma's coolers: chocolate; cough drops; Capri sun; magazines with reports about the rich and beautiful hanging about somewhere on a beach in Italy, all of them with their own car, and all of them free to go on holiday alone. Just as I've really got into one of the stories (I'm practically lying on the white sandy beach myself with a shell on my belly button), the corner of my eye starts **itching**. It's itching because I've seen something which is important. Not consciously. I just see it out of the corner of my eye. It goes without saying that I look over straight away, and I spot the cute guy who supposedly waved at Hella, the guy from the ultra-fast BMW, Bubbles.

---

supposedly – angeblich; to vacuum clean – staubsaugen;
to itch – jucken

I immediately duck behind the salt sticks. My heart is in my mouth, **pounding** far too quickly. What a **coincidence**!

I cautiously peer over my barricade. He hasn't spotted me. He's completely absorbed in the four million **brands** of chewing gum on offer, and he's much cuter than he was in passing.

What am I supposed to think? What am I supposed to do? I can't just let him choose his chewing gum, pay and go! This pounding heart just can't let that happen. This heart which is pounding all because of someone whose father overtook us on the inside and who I first saw through a car window and now from behind.

Actually, why am I **hiding**?

Bubbles reaches out to take something off the shelf. If I let him take that gum over to the cash desk, it'll be too late. But he puts it back, and I try to pull myself together. That was a clear sign. I've been given another chance, and this time I'm not going to waste it – give or take the risk of a heart attack. I'll just go over and apologise for my Dad and his awful behaviour. In fact, I'll go right now.

Bubbles turns around. I duck down instinctively. It just happened.

Don't be **ridiculous**, I think. I'll go over there now.

---

to pound – klopfen, pochen; coincidence – Zufall;
brand – Marke, Sorte; to hide – sich verstecken;
ridiculous – lächerlich, albern

With my newspapers, chocolate and other **bits and bobs**, I stroll over to Bubbles.

At first he doesn't notice me, because he´s still looking at the chewing gums.

I plant myself right next to him. "There must be some that don't **stick** when they burst." Not bad!

Bubbles looks at me. He hasn't got the **foggiest idea** what's going on. He doesn't **know me from Adam.** Then he breaks into a smile from ear to ear. "Hey, you're that girl from the Passat!" He does recognise me.

"We're buying a new car soon!" I lie. We'll never buy a new car.

Bubbles shrugs his shoulders. "Passat is OK!" He grins and just looks at me, which **robs** me of any ability to carry out a **sensible** conversation.

"I just wanted...!" All of a sudden, a tornado comes **swirling** towards us. An express train crashes in between me and Bubbles. My sister Hella.

"Hey, you're that guy from the BMW!" she squeals and pats him on the shoulder as if they'd been **buddies** for ages. "We're buying a new one soon!"

Bubbles grins at me. A secret between the two of us. Hella doesn't seem to have noticed anything, "So? Going to Italy as well?"

---

bits and bobs – dies und das; to stick – kleben;
foggiest idea – leiseste Ahnung; to not know sb from Adam – jmdn. überhaupt nicht kennen; to rob – klauen, berauben; sensible – vernünftig; to swirl – wirbeln; buddies – Kumpel

She's **off her rocker**! What is she talking about? Italy **my giddy aunt**!

Bubbles **scrutinises** her for a second, then he turns away, takes a packet of chewing gum, tosses it into the air and catches it (amazing – I would have dropped it). "Are you going to Italy as well?" He winks at me, shrugs his shoulders and goes over to the cash desk.

Hella grabs his arm and holds him back. She gives him the brightest smile she's got. "Would you like an ice-cream? **It's on me**!" That's always her stupid last **resort** when she notices she's not getting anywhere. As if an ice-cream was the world.

"Sorry, got to go!" Bubbles **gives her the brush-off**, pays and goes. He turns around one last time in the door, smiles at me and waves goodbye.

The door closes. Automatically.

Hella and I just stand there as if turned to stone. Hella because of the cold-shoulder and me because I can't believe that was it, that Hella just did that to me, and that I'm still standing here. So what am I waiting for?

I run off after him in the hope of getting his name, his telephone number or anything.

Hella grabs my arm. "You don't seriously want to

---

to be off one's rocker – nicht mehr alle Tassen im Schrank haben; my giddy aunt – von wegen!;
to scrutinise – mustern; it's on me – ich lad dich ein;
resort – Zuflucht;
to give sb the brush-off – jmdn. abblitzen lassen

go after him, do you? Just because that cool guy showed you a few teeth?" she squeals. "That guy's a **slimeball**, believe me. I know **blokes** like him…"

I wriggle free. "You're just **cheesed off** because he doesn't fancy you!" I run through the automatic doors and see the BMW disappearing into the distance. He's gone.

Hella puts her arm around my shoulders. "See? It's not worth it!"

I go back to the shop as if in a trance and put everything back that I wanted to buy. Instead I just take a packet of chewing gum, the same ones as Bubbles, and **slink** over to the car. **Shuffle. Creep.**

"Get a move on! We haven't got all day! Where have you all been? Having a holiday in the service station?" Why not? If Bubbles were there too!

I throw myself down onto the back seat and chew as slowly as possible, as if I were chewing Bubbles himself.

Grandma Hilde comes out of the toilet with Nightlife in her arms and waves cheerfully.

"Slow-moving traffic on your motorway!" the radio traffic service informs us.

We slowly set off, and Dad starts getting worked up again, because if we hadn't stopped, then we would have missed the slow-moving traffic.

---

slimeball – Schleimer; bloke – Kerl, Typ;
to be cheesed off – sauer sein; to slink – schleichen;
to shuffle – schlurfen; to creep – kriechen

"Nightlife, did you hear that? He's talking about you!" **complains** Grandma Hilde, and Nightlife starts howling again.

I add a second chewing gum to the first one.

Everything is like it always was, and yet everything is different. Bubbles has burst into the unchanging monotony of my holiday, and I can't just wish him away. What would have happened if Hella had fallen **head-over-heels** in love with a biker and **given** the service area shop **a miss**? She'd be sitting **astride** his wheels right now, riding off to far away Headphone Country where talk is **superfluous** and no one can hear anyway. Then Bubbles and I could have continued talking in peace. Then he wouldn't have left so soon, I'm sure.

I put the third piece of chewing gum into my mouth. I can feel Hella eyeing me up from the side again and again, but I don't deign to give her a single look. Because she didn't fall for a biker.

"Hungry?" shrieks Grandma Hilde.

Nightlife immediately stops howling, because he senses dinnertime. He moves over onto my lap so that Grandma Hilde can plunder the first cooler and **share out** the goodies.

"Not hungry," I mumble through my mass of chewing gum.

---

to complain – sich beklagen; head-over-heels – Hals über Kopf; to give a miss – etwas auslassen; astride – rittlings; superfluous – überflüssig; to share out – austeilen

Hella rolls her eyes with a look that says: *Oh, Madame's lost her appetite, because she's looovesick*!

It's just **as well** for her she doesn't say it aloud. Yes, she's doing herself a favour. Really. She can **count her lucky stars** that I haven't gone for her throat yet. She's ruined my life. Maybe Bubbles was the man of my life? When my heart pounds like that, well, that's not normal! And the way he smiled at me, he obviously didn't find me completely **repellent**. He didn't smile at Hella. So it's as simple as that: I met the man of my life in a service area, and I've lost him already. If Hella hadn't have turned up we would have told each other our names and exchanged telephone numbers. I would have spent all holiday thinking about him in Austria, and he about me in... Italy. I would barely have got home, and the telephone would have rung. It would be him. A date, a kiss, later a wedding and then annual holidays with the rich and beautiful in Italy. Damn and blast!

I add the next piece of chewing gum to the **glob** in my mouth and feel closer to Bubbles. I feel closer to him because his father's BMW is two cars in front of us, creeping along in the slow-moving traffic.

It **hits me like a bullet**. He's back. No joke. And it's probably my very last chance.

---

as well – nur gut; to count one's lucky stars – von Glück reden können; repellent – abstoßend; glob – Klumpen; it hits me like a bullet – mich trifft fast der Schlag

All of a sudden I sit **bolt upright** and stare out of the front windscreen. I don't want to lose sight of him, not for a second. I even manage to catch a glimpse of his head between the two **rear headrests**, and my heart starts pounding like crazy.

Nightlife **farts** on my lap because my new upright sitting position doesn't seem to be quite so comfortable for him. Everybody groans because Nightlife's farts stink. **Revolted** I push Nightlife over to Grandma Hilde, and she comes to the conclusion that the poodle needs to go to the toilet.

"No!" says Dad.

I peer over to Hella. Has she seen him? Unlikely. She'd never be able to hold back some comment or other. She's just looking indifferently out of her window, bobbing up and down to the music in her headphones.

All of a sudden she screws up her nose. "Nightlife's farted!" she shrieks and everybody shouts back, "Oh no!"

Only Grandma **disputes** the fact and complains that Nightlife is always given the **blame** for everything.

Which all means that Hella really hasn't seen him. I don't let him out of my sight.

---

bolt upright – kerzengerade;
rear headrest – hintere Kopfstütze; to fart – furzen;
revolted – angewidert; to dispute – in Frage stellen;
blame – Schuld

"They should let people know that this has developed into a major traffic jam! Then people could find a **diversion**!" grumbles Dad.

"There's a major traffic jam on your motorway," announces the radio traffic service. "Please take the alternative route to the nearest motorway at the next junction!"

Every year on our way to our Austrian holiday we get the same announcement. And every year there follows a debate about whether it's smarter to take the recommended diversion or to stay put on the same motorway. What will the others do? That's the million-dollar question. But this year there's more to lose than a million dollars. We just have to do whatever that BMW in front of us does. That's all important. And it's also why this year I **throw myself into** the debate with all I've got.

Mum tries to spread out the map over Tom and Jerry's cage because Dad – as is the case every year – insists that she checks to see if there's a third possibility. Tom and Jerry hop around nervously, and Mum **has a go at** Dad because Tom and Jerry are hopping around nervously because she has to look at the map. Nightlife starts howling. He has to go for a pee, says Grandma Hilde. But no one pays her the slightest attention.

---

diversion – Umleitung;
to throw oneself into – sich einmischen;
to have a go at sb – jmdn. beschimpfen

I keep staring out of the front windscreen as **inconspicuously** as possible and try to guess what the BMW is going to do. Bubbles also seems to be struggling with a road map, at least there's considerable movement in his car. An announcement like this always provokes the same reaction: people's desperate need to find the right solution – and preferably a better one than anybody else.

A blue sign warns of the approaching junction. The decision is getting closer. I see Bubbles pointing to the right. They want to leave the motorway.

"I'd take the diversion," I say to Dad quickly.

"Since when have you been interested in navigating?" Mum asks as she folds up the map. "I **can't make head or tail of** this."

"The other motorway's better. It's logical. Listen, everybody's heard this announcement, and everybody thinks that everybody else is going to take the diversion. That's why they're going to decide to stay put here. It's just common sense."

"Perfect common sense," **regurgitates** Grandma Hilde, but only because she's realised that there's no service area on this motorway for miles.

"The others have probably come up with exactly the same logic, **smart ass**," barks Hella. "And that's why they'll all take the diversion."

---

inconspicuously – unauffällig;
to make head or tail of sth – aus etwas schlau werden;
to regurgitate – nachplappern; smart ass – Klugscheißer

I hate Hella.

"Then it would be better to stay here," concludes Mum.

The BMW starts **indicating**. They're turning off.

"My God, every year we stay put on the motorway with the traffic jam, and every year it's a disaster! Can't we just do it differently for once?"

Everybody looks at me. Hella is grinning slightly.

Stop grinning like that Hella.

"Didn't we take the diversion the year before last?" asks Mum.

Hella nods.

"That makes no difference. Sophie's right. Let's take the diversion!" **butts in** Grandma Hilde.

My father starts indicating.

The BMW stops indicating. They've changed their mind.

Hella is grinning at me.

"Are you doing an impression of a horse, or what's with the stupid smile?" I snap at her. "Gran's wrong. We have to stay put on the motorway."

"Whaaat?" No one can draw out an *aaa* longer than my mum. "What are you talking about, Sophie? Are you **pulling our leg**?"

Dad's getting nervous.

"No, she just wants us to follow the BMW..." shrieks Hella.

---

to indicate – anzeigen, hier: blinken; to butt in – einwerfen; to pull one's leg – Späße treiben mit jmdm.

"Shut up!" I **roar** at her.

The car before us turns off. The BMW is now right in front of our nose.

"...because the guy who was **chatting her up** in the service area is in the back seat."

"I beg your pardon?" Dad turns around to me **frowning** so hard that his eyebrows form a single line. "Is that true?"

Bang. A collision. Passat into a BMW.

Now that's a new situation. And it's my big chance. It's fallen into my lap **out of the blue,** and now I couldn't care less if Hella **spilled the beans** or not. **Big deal**. Who cares? Bubbles didn't try to chat me up.

Dad, of course, **hits the roof**. He jumps out of the car and **hurls abuse** at the man in the BMW. "What do you think you're doing, braking for no reason like that!? It's unbelievable. First you drive like the devil was on your heels and then you brake for no reason!" And so forth.

For some reason he seems to have completely forgotten that he wasn't looking ahead at the time. He was, in fact, looking back at me, but it wasn't my fault. Hella's to blame for that. Besides, people do have to brake occasionally, even in slow-moving

---

to roar – brüllen; to chat sb up – jmdn. anbaggern;
to frown – die Stirn runzeln; out of the blue – aus heiterem Himmel; to spill the beans – petzen;
big deal – was soll's, na und?; to hit the roof – an die Decke gehen; to hurl abuse – wüst beschimpfen

traffic, because if you don't, then you drive right into the car in front. Simple as that. Bubbles' Dad tries to explain this to my father, although his tone of voice is **a touch** too loud. My dad doesn't let people explain things to him at that volume.

The cars behind us begin to beep their horns, even though there's already a traffic jam and no one's getting anywhere anyway.

Grandma Hilde gets out of the car with Nightlife. They slip off into the bushes. Mum makes sure Tom and Jerry haven't been injured in the accident.

I glance **scornfully** at my sister. It's my *you're-a-sad-case* look, and then I get out of the car with a heart that's about to explode. I can't wait to see Bubbles again. He's sitting in the BMW, shaking his head. He has no intention of getting out of the car, because he wants nothing to do with the argument. But then he sees me looking at him and smiling at him, and all of a sudden the situation is different. At least that's the impression I get. Anyway, he gets out of the car and comes and stands next to me. I quickly have to get rid of the glob of chewing gum. It looks stupid.

Bubbles looks at the non-existent **damage**. There's nothing there, not even a **scratch**. He rolls his eyes and smiles to himself. And then I roll my eyes and do an impression of a horse.

---

a touch – hier: eine Spur; scornfully – verächtlich;
damage – Schaden; scratch – Kratzer

"Hey, there's no damage!" Bubbles tries to interrupt our fathers' heated argument, but they don't hear him (which may have something to do with the four million other cars in the traffic jam which are now all beeping their horns).

"And anyway, it's all the fault of your badly behaved son. **Pestering** my young daughter at the service area. **Seduction of a minor**, that's what it is!"

I **freeze**. All of a sudden, I feel really cold. Ice cubes rattle along my **veins**. Everything moves in slow motion.

The voices around me start to vibrate through the air: *Uauuauuauuuaa*.

Bubbles looks at me in **amazement**. Amazed – *a bit*. **Disappointed** – *very*.

Hella leans against the car and watches everything without blinking an eyelid. She can hide her **malicious joy** well.

"It that true?" Bubbles' father looks at him **sternly**.

This can't be true! How is it possible for everything to go so wrong? I want to intervene and say "that's not true, of course not," but I can't even make a sound.

"That's not true!" says Bubbles frostily as he gets

---

to pester – belästigen; seduction of a minor – Verführung Minderjähriger; to freeze – hier: erstarren; vein – Ader; amazement – Erstaunen; disappointed – enttäuscht; malicious joy – Schadenfreude; sternly – streng

back into the BMW. "Why should I do a thing like that?" No more smiles for Sophie – no reason why he should – but he didn't have to make that last comment. It's not that **implausible**, is it?

In any case the party slowly breaks up, because the police arrive and want to take down all the **particulars**. This isn't really in anyone's interest, so we reach an agreement (that is, we have completely differing opinions), **take refuge** in our car and drive on.

I'm **devastated**. I hate my family. You can't go around saying things like that! Dad's got no right to stick his nose into my business. Hella neither. Particularly not Hella.

"Everything OK, Sophie?" asks Mum, and when I don't reply – because if I did, I would burst into tears – she turns around. "Stop the car. At once!"

Do I look that bad?

"We forgot Grandma!"

Oh, right.

Fortunately the flow of traffic hasn't got any better, and we can see Grandma in the distance running back along the **hard shoulder**, waving her granny shoe.

Hella hangs out of the window and cheers her

---

implausible – unglaubwürdig; particulars – Personalien;
to take refuge – Zuflucht suchen;
devastated – völlig am Boden zerstört;
hard shoulder – Seitenstreifen

on, clapping her hands and whistling through her fingers. "Go, go, go! You can make it, Grandma!"

One day that girl's going to **get a clip around the ear** from someone, and a big fat one at that. Because she's nasty, and she enjoys making other people unhappy with all that **nastiness** of hers. There was absolutely no need to tell Dad about Bubbles. It was completely unnecessary, and she didn't actually get anything from it. It was just downright nasty.

Grandma Hilde and Nightlife finally **catch up with** us. They're completely out of breath, but Grandma still manages to hit Hella with her shoe. Not really properly. Just for fun. But, of course, Hella **kicks up a huge fuss**.

Grandma squeezes in between us and shows me the sole of her shoe. "Someone spat out a huge lump of chewing gum."

I guess the situation really is quite funny, and we should be having a good laugh about it, but to be honest I'm just not in a joking mood. I can't bear Dad's **angry tirade** any longer: about the slow-moving traffic; about Grandma's chewing gum and chewing gum in general; about the missed diversion; and about the BMW, which right now seems

---

to get a clip around the ear – eins auf die Rübe kriegen; nastiness – Gemeinheit; to catch up with sb – jmdn. einholen; to kick up a huge fuss – großes Theater machen; angry tirade – Schimpfkanonade

to be in a faster moving lane as it overtakes us triumphantly.

I immediately **make myself scarce** behind Mum's kitchen towel. Of course, he won't look over. He wouldn't even **deem** me **worthy** of a glance. *What an utter nutcase! Silly cow! Dumb chick!* That's probably what he thinks of me. That is, if he can even be bothered to waste a thought on me. Still, just in case he does happen to look over, I want to make sure I'm not there.

"Hey, how about a song?" suggests Grandma Hilde, because the **nagging** is starting to get on her nerves, too.

Mum, Dad and Grandma: "Leaving behind the grey cities of Mauhauern, we pass through woods and fields…!"

I don't **join in**. Definitely not. Not me, and not Tom and Jerry either.

"A warning to drivers: traffic on the motorway is now at a complete standstill. Cars are **bumper** to bumper. Please turn off your engines and remain calm!" Everybody stops singing.

"Shit, shit, shit!" My dad keeps beeping the horn, and Mum is completely **oblivious** to his bad lan-

---

to make yourself scarce – auf Tauchstation gehen;
to deem sb worthy – jmdn. für würdig erachten;
utter nutcase – Wahnsinnige/-r; dumb chick – blödes Huhn;
nagging – Gemotze; to join in – mitmachen, sich beteiligen;
bumper – Stoßstange; oblivious – gleichgültig

guage. "Why didn't we take the diversion?" He turns off the engine.

Silence.

It's never ever been this quiet in the car. No one **utters** a sound. Even Hella. I can't bear it. I clap my hands together, and Grandma is so **startled** that Nightlife begins to howl. Thank God.

"Let's unpack our things and have a picnic on the motorway!" I suggest. I've decided to give up on Bubbles. I'll just stop thinking about him. No more suffering. I'll pretend he never even existed. Bubbles? Who is Bubbles?

Everybody is **thrilled** with my idea. Mum and Grandma immediately **get stuck into** the coolers, and Dad rolls out his sleeping bag as a picnic blanket. Hella spots a guy with a guitar two cars down who she considers to be really cool looking. He offers to play us a serenade for lunch – at least with his tongue – and Mum starts to feel sick.

Tom and Jerry remain in the Passat as it's supposedly too hot for them outside. Nightlife is **given a free rein**, which is why people keep coming up to us to complain (he keeps peeing against their cars). As **compensation** they're given an egg or a spoonful of strawberry *fromage frais* and off they go.

---

to utter – äußern; startled – erschrocken; thrilled – begeistert; to get stuck into sth – sich über etwas hermachen; to give a free rein to sb – jmdm. freie Hand lassen; compensation – Entschädigungsleistung

"They're all a bit **overwrought**," says Grandma.

Everyone except us.

Maybe Bubbles is also stuck in the traffic jam. Or maybe they managed to get through. I shake my head and stick my little finger into my ear as if it was plugged up with water. Got to get rid of that thought. Like I never had it.

"I'm going for a walk," shouts Hella. It seems the guitarist with the gift of tongues is, in fact, a little too **wacko** for her. "Maybe I'll see...," she gives me a nod, "... you know who!" She must have a really **bad conscience**.

"Don't you dare!" Like I said, I'm putting him out of my mind. In fact, I've already forgotten him.

Two kids are playing *Catch me if you can, you prat!* around our car. One car further down, a young couple are having an argument because the guy wants to see if he can fry an egg on the car roof. It's that hot. The radio traffic service makes an announcement: "The friendly traffic angels are going to be bringing cold drinks to your motorway!"

That's no bad thing. Our coolers are anything but cool anymore. More like **insulation boxes**.

All of a sudden, the woman one car up hurls all six eggs against the windscreen. I don't think she quite got the point.

---

overwrought – überreizt; wacko – durchgeknallt;
bad conscience – schlechtes Gewissen;
insulation boxes – Warmhaltekisten

"I can't see him anywhere!" shouts Hella with a shrug of her shoulders as she **threads** her way back through the cars. "Looks like they got through!"

Dad instantly turns red in the face and is just about to go off on a **rant** again about how the devil always shits in the same place and how money rules the world and so forth, when Grandma Hilde stuffs a **pickled gherkin** into his mouth. "Spare us. We all know what you want to say."

Nightlife sits down next to her and successfully **acquires** all the hot dogs. Mum is still singing the song from the car, and I'm happy that Hella didn't find Bubbles. Who knows what she'd have got up to on her bad-conscience trip. Maybe she would have **turned up** with him. That's all I need. Now that I've already forgotten him.

The *catch me if you can* boys have disappeared all of a sudden, and Jerry with them, because the boys opened the cage **just for a laugh**. Mum and I spot this at the same time. She immediately rushes over to the cage, screaming, and slams the cage door shut so that at least Tom doesn't fly off as well. Then she starts calling **frantically** after Jerry, blowing kisses into the air.

---

to thread – sich schlängeln; rant – Wortschwall;
pickled gherkin – Essiggurke;
to acquire – sich aneignen, besorgen;
to turn up – aufkreuzen; just for a laugh – nur aus Spaß;
frantically – verzweifelt

Of course, there's now no way we can continue our picnic. The clock is ticking to find Jerry before Mum goes officially **insane**.

"Do you want me to **beat up** those boys?" shrieks Hella, as if that would really help. We can't even prove it was them. Though, who else could it have been?

"We can coordinate a **search party**," suggests Dad, waving his arms around in the air and barking orders. Everybody gets a handful of bird food and is sent off in a different direction.

Grandma Hilde lets Nightlife sniff at Tom. "Find, Nightlife! Find!"

The poodle does actually manage to **pick up a trail**, and he drags Grandma resolutely towards the bushes at the edge of the motorway.

I'm sent off straight ahead. I hold my handful of bird food high into the air, hoping Jerry might smell it. Every now and again I call out his name. But I soon realise what an embarrassing sight I must be, walking through a traffic jam with a hand above my head calling "Jerry!" It's not even possible to say the name "Jerry" normally in a situation like this. You have to make two words out of it: Jer Ry. Stupid name.

It's also extremely difficult to walk, because most

---

insane – wahnsinnig; to beat up – verhauen;
search party – Suchtrupp;
to pick up a trail – eine Fährte aufnehmen

of the people are hanging out in their cars with their legs stretched out. Looking up for Jerry – where I imagine him to be – **poses** a constant danger.

Some guy is doing the rounds offering to braid women's hair with colourful threads. No one's really interested. It'd be a lot smarter if he had something to drink!

Then the **inevitable** happens. I trip and fall flat on my face. I drop all the bird food, and the fat guy whose legs I've tripped over has a go at me. "Can't you watch where you're going, you **wally**?"

I'm just about to get back on my feet and **give him a piece of my mind** – stupid **fatso**, he should watch where he puts his feet – when I see HIM. The Forgotten One. The One I never met. Bubbles.

He's leaning against the boot of the BMW, which is also stuck in the traffic jam, despite the fact that it was so expensive. Jerry is wriggling around in Bubbles' hair. Without singing. Bubbles doesn't move a muscle. He stands there like he's made of stone, staring at me steadily.

"Don't move," I whisper to him, although Bubbles clearly isn't planning on moving anywhere, and I slowly **tiptoe** over to him. I slowly tiptoe up to the guy who I only recently forgot, the guy who

---

to pose – darstellen; the inevitable – das Unvermeidbare;
wally – Vollidiot;
to give sb a piece of one's mind – jmdm. die Meinung sagen;
fatso – Fettsack; to tiptoe – auf Zehenspitzen gehen

is still making my heart pound like crazy. So much for that!

Bubbles looks at me.

Jerry turns around, plucks at Bubbles' hair and acts as if everything was alright, or as if he were checking to see how long the traffic jam is so that he can make an announcement on the radio traffic service. The bird doesn't see how close I come. So close, I can feel Bubbles' breath. So close, I can smell how good he smells. So close, I can **pluck up all** my **courage** and apologise. For Hella, my father and the terrible lie.

Bubbles can't move, because otherwise Jerry would fly off. He has to listen to me whether he wants to or not.

Then I grab Jerry, pure and simple. He settles calmly in my cupped hands and looks at me.

Now Bubbles could move if he wanted to. Or even talk. He could say that everything's OK, and that he knew all the time that I had nothing to do with my Dad's lie. He could do something. Anything. But he does nothing. He just stands there and looks at me.

I wait and return his **gaze** until I can't take it anymore. Right then. I'll be off. A cautious smile, but Bubbles doesn't smile back. I turn around and head slowly back towards the Passat where my frantic mother is waiting for her Jerry.

---

pluck up all courage – allen Mut zusammennehmen;
gaze – Blick

My **head is buzzing with thoughts**. They shoot out left, right and centre, colliding into each other, flying back and forth, boing, boing, boing. Bubbles has **got a grudge** against me. The **insinuation** that he tried to chat me up obviously really got under his skin. He can't forgive me. Ever. If he ends up owning a kiosk and is sitting behind the counter aged 98 without a hair on his head and I happen to turn up to buy a packet of chewing gum, then he won't even look at me. That's how bad his grudge is against me. Or else he never really wanted anything from me in the first place. He thought I was ugly and stupid from the very start. It was all just a trick of my imagination. Or maybe that was exactly what he found so charming about me – the way I crept up to him and **rendered** him **speechless**. Rubbish. Idiot. Bubbles has burst. Dead.

Mum carefully takes Jerry out of my hands and puts him into the cage next to Tom. Then she gives me a big hug. She's **over the moon**. "Did he sing? I thought maybe he would have sung in freedom!"

He didn't. He just **gawked**.

The other search parties slowly return after not having found Jerry. Only Grandma and Nightlife are

---

one's head is buzzing with thoughts – einem schwirren alle möglichen Gedanken durch den Kopf;
to have a grudge against sb – einen Groll auf jmdn. haben;
insinuation – Unterstellung; to render sb speechless – jmdn. sprachlos machen; to be over the moon – außer sich sein vor Freude; to gawk – gaffen

still missing, but we agree **unanimously** not to undertake any more search operations. They'll turn up.

"Did you see him?" squeals Hella.

I shrug my shoulders pretending not to know who she means. Then I sit down in the middle of the motorway, **prop** myself **up** against the wheels of our old Passat and bury myself in my book. At least I pretend to do so. It goes without saying that I can't concentrate at all. Not knowing that the 'dead' Bubbles is in the **vicinity**.

The others have a bite to eat, and Mum **whistles** the family song to Tom and Jerry.

At some point Grandma Hilde turns up with Nightlife, completely out of breath, her hair a real mess. "Nightlife lost the trail!"

"Jerry's back, Mummy. Sophie found him," says Mum as she eases Grandma down onto the front seat.

"You could have told me that before!" she **moans** as she kicks off her granny shoes.

"The friendly traffic angels have arrived with cold drinks!" announces the radio traffic service.

Because I'm feeling a bit sorry for Grandma I offer to go and look for the van and get us some refreshments.

"I'll come with you," squeals Hella, and I don't really care if she does or not.

---

unanimously – einstimmig; to prop up – anlehnen;
in the vicinity – in der Nähe; to whistle – pfeifen;
to moan – klagen

We walk down the **congested** motorway side by side without saying a word. It doesn't take us long to spot a horrifically long queue of people waiting for their cold drinks. Bubbles is not amongst them, though it wouldn't make any difference if he were. **As far as I'm concerned**, Bubbles is dead. I don't want to have anything to do with people who bear grudges. They're usually **stingy** as well, and there's nothing worse than that.

"Listen, Sophie, I'm sorry about what happened with the BMW guy." My sister has taken off her headphones and is talking at normal volume. She just apologised! That's never happened before! Not in my lifetime. "I know it might be inexcusable, but the guy was really cute, and he clearly **fancied** you ..."

That's not what I want to hear. It's just not true. And Hella doesn't have to go on for ever. "Already forgotten!" I don't bear grudges. Not me.

There are only four hundred and eighty-five people still in front of us in the queue.

Hella puts the headphones back into her ears, grins slightly and raises her hand. "I'm off!"

What's that for? **She's nuts**. She can't just leave me here all on my own! I shouldn't have just said everything was alright. "Hey, wait a second, I can't forgive you that easily...!"

---

congested – verstopft; as far as I'm concerned – was mich angeht; stingy – geizig; to fancy sb – auf jmdn. stehen; to be nuts – durchgeknallt sein

But Hella's gone, and all of a sudden I know why.

Bubbles taps me on my shoulder. "Hi. Waiting for a cold drink, too?"

My heart immediately starts beating like crazy. I try to calm myself down – after all, Bubbles is 'dead' for me, I don't feel anything for him anymore – but I have to concentrate to stay on my feet.

Bubbles just lingers next to me. He doesn't seem to mind that I'm not paying him any attention at all. "That was stupid **just now**."

My heart!

"I couldn't get a sound out. It was a really strange situation, and you looked..."

What? Tell me! Spit it out!

"...you looked really sweet."

Explosion! Bubbles is alive. Bubbles is great. Bubbles is **beyond belief**!

I look at him, and he looks at me, and we decide to go for a walk, away from the others, away from the queue. Grandma Hilde will just have to wait for her cold drink.

Bubbles goes ahead and holds open the bush at the edge of the motorway for me, like the Prince in **Sleeping Beauty**. Bubbles is the only person who can overcome the motorway **hedge** with his sword. I knew that from the very start.

---

just now – vorhin;
beyond belief – unglaublich;
Sleeping Beauty – Dornröschen; hedge – Hecke

On the other side of the hedge is a **paddock** where two white horses are galloping to and fro, chasing each other and playfully biting each other's necks.

We sit down in the grass and watch them. There's nothing we can think of to say.

I pluck a few blades of grass and weave a **plait** out of them that no one needs. "You know… that canary, he doesn't sing. That kills my mum."

Bubbles grins. "He can't sing because he's a *she*. And female canaries don't sing. Ever."

I stare at him. "Jerry's a girl?"

"Jerry's a girl."

We laugh. All of a sudden, Bubbles takes my hand. The laughter gets stuck in my throat and collides into my pounding heart which is on its way up.

"You know what? I thought you were really sweet right from the very start."

Boy, he doesn't have any **inhibitions**. He just comes right out with it.

"Me, too," I say in a **squeaky** voice, and quickly clear my throat to get my voice back from wherever it's gone. It's probably stuck in my throat, together with my laughter and my heart.

"Do you think I could kiss you?"

Oh boy! Sure. Do it. Don't ask. Go ahead!

He turns my face to his and looks me in the eyes.

---

paddock – Koppel; plait – Zopf; inhibition – Hemmung; squeaky – kieksig

I can't hold his gaze. I look away to something below. **He's just about** to kiss me. I'm on my way to seventh heaven.

But all of a sudden, a million cars start their engines.

We jump to our feet.

"Shit, they're moving on!"

I guess we're the only two who aren't pleased about this **turn of events**. We look at each other thinking the same thing. Just for a second: let them go. Off into their holidays. We're staying here. We won't go back. Bubbles can start working here as a **stable hand** – I always wanted a stable boy – and I can help gather apples at **harvest** time. We'd be as happy as can be. We could live in the **barn**, upstairs in the hay. We wouldn't need a TV or anything, because we'd have each other. At some point we'll write a postcard home to our parents telling them not to worry. When we get married later, we'll invite them to the wedding, but by then we'll have our own **stud farm**.

"Hey! Sophie! Get your backside over here! We're moving on!" Hella is standing at the hedge, waving at us.

Bubbles and I look at each other.

"Quick!"

---

to be just about – im Begriff sein, etwas zu tun; turn of events – Wendung der Ereignisse; stable hand – Stallknecht; harvest – Ernte; barn – Scheune; stud farm – Gestüt

A cacophony of car horns. Again.

We start running up the embankment to the motorway. There's no time left. Not even to exchange a telephone number, an address, anything.

"So what's he called?" asks Hella when we're sitting on the back seat of the car **heading** towards Austria.

I don't know. I don't even know his name. Then I start to cry.

In Austria everything is as it always is. Only I'm different. I'm lovesick and in a bad mood every day, 24 hours a day, mainly about myself. Why didn't I at least ask him his name? Why am I standing here **empty-handed**? I have absolutely no way of trying to find him. Him, the boy who almost kissed me. That was what confused me. That's why I couldn't think straight. The kiss. The it-didn't-quite-happen kiss.

On day three of our Austrian holiday we always go on a big mountain hike. All of us together. With no exception. Except Tom and Jerry of course (whose **standing** has risen since becoming female). They were allowed to stay at home wrapped in cotton wool.

Actually I love this mountain hike, but this time

---

to head – ansteuern;
empty-handed – mit leeren Händen;
standing – Stellenwert

I really **don't feel like it**. I have no desire to **trudge behind** my chaotic family. I just want to be on my own for once – just for myself – to think things through and develop a new strategy for how to get over Bubbles. Bubbles! What a stupid name!

Everybody's ready and waiting at the breakfast table in the guest house.

"I'd like to stay here!" I just give it a try. It won't work, but then at least I'll have said it.

Everybody nods and Grandma leaves Nightlife behind to protect me.

Rather **at a loss** I wave goodbye to my family as they head off towards the mountains. Watching them disappear I almost burst into tears again. How's this meant **to work out**? How am I going to forget *him* now?

I walk slowly through the Austrian village with Nightlife and think about *him* lying on the beach in Italy, having long forgotten me. That kills me. I'll never forget *him*. Never! I stare sullenly at the ground and end up **bumping into** someone.

"Hey, can't you look where you're going?!" I snap and look up to see what kind of an idiot has crossed my path.

---

not to feel like doing sth – keine Lust auf etwas haben;
to trudge behind – hinterhertrotten; at a loss – fassungslos;
to work out – klappen, gelingen;
to bump into – zusammenstoßen, hineinrennen

Nightlife is **barking his guts out** and is about to kill the attacker. But thank God he's only a poodle. I wouldn't want him to attack the person in front of me.

It's Bubbles. He holds his hand to his head.

When he recognises me, he breaks into a huge smile. "You? What are you doing here?"

"And you? I thought I'd never see you again!"

It turns out that Bubbles also lied when he said they were going to Italy. "Your sister really got on my nerves with her **bragging**."

This is wonderful! I can't believe it! How many more times do we have to lose each other and find each other again, even though we've given up all hope of ever seeing each other again? It should never happen again. Never, ever!

Bubbles takes my hand. "Do you think I could kiss you now? I haven't stopped thinking about it since I saw you."

But I can't right now. I tear a piece of paper and pen out of my rucksack and hand him both items. "First I need your telephone number. Just in case you run off again!"

Bubbles grins at me and starts writing.

"And your name as well, OK?" I whisper, fighting the **tingly feeling** in my stomach. "What's your name?"

---

to bark his guts out – sich die Seele aus dem Leib bellen; bragging – Angeberei; tingly feeling – Kribbeln

Christamaria Fiedler

Kissing Crime

All the girls in 7b **fell in love** last holiday! Saskia and Binette with a Portuguese **waiter**, Lola with the brother of a friend of hers, Rose with a Roman pizza **chef**. Lisa was **head-over-heels** in love with an exchange student, Sophie with a Danish DJ, Henriette with a **Dutch** high-school student, and Jennifer Niemann with no less than a kissing stranger! Only Isy and Amanda **missed the boat**. And at **break** time just about everybody had something to tell them with a certain smile. Only Isy and Amanda didn't smile.

They'd spent the best weeks of the year on the mysterious trail of an **alleged** criminal and had forgotten about everything else. A mistake which, according to Amanda, they shouldn't repeat again this summer.

They were now sitting under a breezy sunshade in front of Signore Georgio's Ristorante, enjoying

---

to fall in love – sich verlieben; waiter – Kellner; chef – Koch;
head-over-heels – Hals über Kopf; Dutch – holländisch;
to miss the boat – den Anschluss verpassen; break – Pause;
alleged – angeblich, vermeintlich

the best ice-cream between Rostock and Rome. Isy had chosen *Kiwi* while Amanda was licking away with **relish** at *Malaga*.

The sky over the city was a vibrant blue. The clouds were floating in it like **cotton wool**.

"Holidays are meant for relaxing," explained Amanda. "And for falling in love!"

"Alright," sighed Isy with consideration. Even hobby detectives had a right to hot holiday flirts.

The traffic roared around their sunshade island. It was a perfectly normal afternoon in Berlin. In two weeks' time everything would be different.

In two weeks' time the schools would close and a **tingling**, **bubbly** wave of excitement would sweep across the city, giving everybody a kind of champagne flush. The first **convoy of cars** would set off towards the sea or the mountains, beeping their horns as they went, while flocks of silver birds would rise high into the sky, carrying their heavy holiday load. Those who hadn't **hit the road** by then would be buying suitcases, trekking shoes, beach balls and sun cream as if there were no tomorrow.

"And where, if you don't mind telling me, are we going to relax and fall in love?" pressed Amanda.

They had already managed to **swap** a respectable

---

relish – Genuss; cotton wool – Watte; tingling – prickelnd;
bubbly – schäumend; convoy of cars – Fahrzeugkonvoi;
to hit the road – sich auf den Weg machen;
to swap – tauschen

report for their parents' permission to go on holiday together, only to join their families later, but there was still some uncertainty about the destination. This wasn't a question of money (they still had quite a bit left from the rewards of their detective work), but was down to differing interests. While Amanda was flirting with the idea of doing a cooking course in Catalonia or a Sushi crash course in Tokyo, Isy had other plans. She had no desire either to learn to cook Catalonian style or **mess about** with sticky rice.

All she dreamed of was doing a course for hobby criminologists at Scotland Yard in the heart of London. But there was one major **drawback**: the course didn't exist yet, and it was very unlikely it ever would.

Yet despite their differing interests, they were both agreed that neither of their suggestions for holiday destinations was particularly **suitable** for falling in love. They'd simply have to find new ones. Isy, however, was **at a loss**.

"What about Rose's Roman pizza chef?" suggested Amanda. "Rome maybe?"

"We don't have to go to Rome for that. There are enough Pizza chefs in Berlin."

"Or that Danish DJ? Copenhagen's meant to be

---

report – Zeugnis; to mess about – herummachen;
drawback – Nachteil; suitable – passend, geeignet;
at a loss – ratlos

well hip! Sophie said he put on her favourite song every time she came into the disco…"

"What if it was **coincidence**?"

"Don't always think the worst!"

"I don't think the worst. I think critically."

That was true. Isy really did think critically. And she was always alert as well, because just then she spotted a thin young man in a red shirt who pulled out of the stream of skaters **whizzing** by. As quick as a **predatory** buzzard, he shot over to the sunshade of their grey-haired neighbour, heading straight for the purse which was lying there like an invitation card next to the glass of coffee ice-cream.

"Watch out! Your money!"

The startled woman quickly grabbed her purse. **Just in the nick of time**.

With a **cheeky** grin the "buzzard" sped off in an elegant curve without his pickings. Maybe he'd have more luck in the next street café.

"Hey, we're not in **Naples** here!" said Amanda **irately**, as Signore Georgio interrupted his service of another table and anxiously hurried over.

"The lady left her purse open," explained Isy, pointing to the spot where the purse had been lying on the small marble table.

---

coincidence – Zufall; to whizz – sausen, flitzen;
predatory – räuberisch;
just in the nick of time – gerade noch rechtzeitig;
cheeky – frech; Naples – Neapel; irately – empört

"It couldn't have been more inviting," added Amanda. "But thanks to Isolde Schütze's famous **eagle eyes** it all turned out for the best..."

"Cara mia!" The padrone patted Isy's hand. "You are very lucky, signora, that Isolde Schütze and her friend Amanda Bornstein are sitting at the next table. The two of them have already caught many a thief."

"The padrone is **exaggerating**," Isy said, trying to **water down** the praise.

"Why do you say that? Wasn't it you two who solved the post office robbery, stopped a falcon being smuggled to Saudi Arabia, exposed the kid-napping of a classmate, and ultimately put the museum thieves **under lock and key**? And didn't you both also get generously **rewarded** for it?"

"Yes, but all that happened more or less accidentally," said Isy **modestly**.

"Rubbish!" added Amanda. "You always smell adventure a mile off and then get us **tangled up** in it! That's why they call us the '**calamity queens**' in our class..."

"You've probably seen a photo of the two young ladies on a front page somewhere, shaking hands

---

eagle eye – Argusauge; to exaggerate – übertreiben;
to water down – abschwächen;
under lock and key – hinter Schloss und Riegel;
rewarded – belohnt; modestly – bescheiden;
to get tangled up in sth – in etwas verwickelt werden;
calamity queens – Katastrophenweiber

with the chief constable," said Signore Georgio to the old lady to kindly end the minor differences.

The old lady nodded, though she didn't look particularly **convinced**. She couldn't recall having seen the tall, blonde girl with the blue eyes and the **dainty** girl with the dark curls, her two temporary guardian angels, anywhere before.

"Thanks ever so much!" She winked at the girls with a guilty conscience. "I'll be more careful next time." Then she asked for a glass of water. The incident had clearly exhausted her.

"A glass of water and three portions of tiramisu for the nerves!" called over Signore Georgio cheerfully to his wife Violetta and took a polite bow. "You'll be feeling much better in a moment, Signora. It's the best tiramisu in town!"

The signore wasn't exaggerating. His tiramisu really was without equal. While Isy was **polishing off** her portion, Amanda brought up the Danish DJ again with her mouth full.

"I don't know," Isy pulled a face. "I think it's pretty uncool."

"Okay, then there's only Sassi and Bini's Portuguese waiter left, or Henriette's Dutch high-school student who can kiss for ten minutes without having to come up for breath..."

"Look, why do we have to copy the others?"

---

convinced – überzeugt; dainty – zierlich;
to polish off – verputzen

"Why not? It saves us time!" There was a crumb of tiramisu on Amanda's upper lip. The **wind picked up** and fluttered under the stiff white tablecloth. "Think about it, we only have a week!"

"If we only have a week and all you want to do is follow in the others' footsteps then..." – at this point Isy took a deep breath – "...then I'm for Jennifer Niemann's kissing stranger. At least that sounds pretty exciting!"

Isy found Jennifer's mysterious hotel story – which had caused quite a **stir** in 7b at the start of the school year – fascinating from the very start. Now she was literally burning with desire to expose the mysterious night-kisser. But Jennifer had already told so much. They had to be careful.

The next day Isy and Amanda grabbed Jennifer at break under the old **horse chestnut tree** just as she was about to bite into her sausage roll. "Hi, Jennifer! Are you going on holiday again this year?"

Jennifer nodded and chewed thoroughly as her eyes darted nervously between her two fellow pupils. Isy and Amanda are **up to something**! She didn't trust them. "A case for two!" "Murder is her

---

the wind picks up – der Wind frischt auf; stir – Aufruhr;
horse chestnut tree – Rosskastanie;
to be up to something – etwas im Schilde führen

hobby!" There was good reason to **gossip** about the two of them in class.

"Are you going to that hotel again where the guy kept creeping into your room in the night to kiss you?"

"No." Jennifer grinned. "My parents want to go to Norway."

"Tell us the story again."

Jennifer rolled her eyes. "I've told it a hundred times!"

"Then tell it for the hundred and first time!"

Pupils of other classes strolled past, chatting away and **slurping** on their drinks noisily. One girl was sobbing into her handkerchief. Sassi and Bini were talking to their highly esteemed class teacher, Dr Trisch, otherwise known as Trischi. So Jennifer Niemann told them the old story again with a sigh. When she'd finished, Isy had **to give her credit** for not leaving anything out and not adding anything either. It was probably the whole truth.

"Did you really never see him?"

"How could I? It was pitch-black in the room. And by the time I was **properly** awake and had turned on the light, he'd gone."

"And what if… it was all just a dream?"

Jennifer pulled a face. "How can you have the same dream every night for a whole week?"

---

to gossip – lästern; to slurp – schlürfen;
to give sb credit – jmdm. als Verdienst anrechnen;
properly – richtig

No, of course not. They both lowered their heads, shamefaced.

"Besides, I found a black hair on my **pillow** twice in the morning!"

"Really! You never mentioned that before!"

"I just remembered it."

"And where is this Forest View Inn?" asked Amanda.

"In Miriquidi."

"Where... er?"

"In the Erz Mountains. The ancient Romans called it the *dark forest*."

Isn't that where the hand-carved Christmas pyramids come from? Isy couldn't help immediately thinking of the funny wooden incense burner in the shape of a little figure and the tasty sweet bread.

"Interesting. Do your parents come from there?"

Jennifer shook her ponytail. "It was an **educational trip**. You could learn traditional Erz **customs** in the hotel."

"What customs?"

"**Lacemaking**, playing the zither, **carving**, **hiking** and baking Hutzen cake."

"And kissing," added Amanda with a grin. "You forgot the most important one."

Isy saw that Sassi and Bini were now on their way

---

pillow – Kopfkissen; educational trip – Bildungsreise; custom – Sitte, Brauch; lacemaking – Spitzenklöppeln; carving – Schnitzen; hiking – Wandern

to the old horse chestnut tree. "Were all the hotel guests kissed in the night?" she quickly asked.

Jennifer blushed. "I think it was just me."

"Why only you?" Amanda eyed up her classmate as if she'd never seen her before. Jennifer wasn't exactly bad looking, but then she wasn't Jennifer Lopez either. "Were you the only female there?"

"Of course not." Jennifer bit into her sandwich, exasperated. "I must have been his type."

That wasn't **to be ruled out**, of course. There was nothing against it.

"And what **floor** did you sleep on?" Isy boldly continued. "Up or downstairs? Stop making it so hard for us."

"Downstairs," choked Jennifer with her mouth full.

"What room number?"

"Seven. Why do you want to know all this?"

"For... er... a **survey** for Allensbach."

"Allensbach?" Jennifer squinted at them suspiciously. She knew all about Isy's ingenious **excuses**.

"I'm sure you've heard of that famous institute for **opinion polls**. Amanda and I are thinking about jobbing there in the holidays. We're just practising with you. But don't mention it to anyone!"

---

to be ruled out – ausgeschlossen sein; floor – hier: Stockwerk; survey – Umfrage; excuses – Ausreden;
opinion polls – Meinungsforschung

Of course Jennifer did mention it to someone. She mentioned it to Rose, and Rose mentioned it to Henriette, and Henriette whispered it into the ears of Sassi and Bini, and within half an hour the whole of 7b knew. So much for Allensbach! Ha! The two calamity queens had a new case!

They probably wanted to find out who had **snogged** Jennifer Niemann night after night last summer! Or – and at the thought of this the entire Year 7 had to hold their breath in excitement – they wanted to be kissed themselves? That was a hot idea!

The calamity queens didn't seem to hear any of the **rumour-mongering** going on about them. They had other concerns. The holidays were starting in two weeks, and they'd have to **get their act together**.

"So the guy has black hair," stated Isy, pouting her lips in thought. "That brings us a bit closer!"

Pleased with their **findings**, the two friends slung their rucksacks over their shoulders and left the classroom. Now they just had to find out where this Forest View Inn was. Maybe the small travel agency on the way home could help them. But the thought of trying to persuade their parents into al-

---

to snog – knutschen; rumour-mongering – Tratsch;
to get sb's act together – Nägel mit Köpfen machen;
finding – Entdeckung

lowing them to take the trip depressed Isy. There was no way they'd be allowed to go on holiday on their own.

"Why don't we just say it's a **school trip**?" suggested Amanda.

"Sure we could do that," admitted Isy. "But I fear there's a **catch**: how do we get to the hotel?"

That was a good point!

They hadn't even left the school building when they **realised** that only their parents would be able to book the holiday anyway. But where else could they find love now? And who would solve the mystery of the nightly kisses in Miriquidi?

They **traipsed** across the schoolyard **dejectedly**. The old horse chestnut tree rustled without a friend in the world. No one was standing in its shadows any longer eating their sandwiches.

Although there was now **no point** in going by the small travel agency anymore, they did just that. The owner was standing in the shop window with her sleeves rolled up, changing the window display. The poster immediately caught their eye. It was advertising a week's stay in a traditional hotel called the Forest View Inn against a background of gentle mountains and dark forests. Speechless, they stared

---

school trip – Klassenfahrt; catch – hier: Haken;
to realise – sich klar werden;
to traipse – schleichen; dejectedly – niedergeschlagen;
no point – keinen Sinn

at the white villa with its turrets and a grey slate roof. At the bottom were the words: 7 nights, 7 courses, 7 meals per day. All inclusive. And at the top in bright red: NOW AT HALF PRICE!

It couldn't be true!

A car stopped and a young couple got out. They took a look at the offer with interest.

"Forget Corfu!" said the young woman enthusiastically. "This sounds really nice!"

"You even get kissed in the night by a stranger there," Amanda informed them. "All inclusive!"

The young couple giggled childishly and disappeared into the small travel agency.

The lucky devils! They'd be able to book without being asked for their ID.

Amanda and Isy continued on their way, looking **as miserable as sin**.

"Actually **I couldn't give a toss** where we fall in love," confessed Amanda. "But at least there it would have been for half price! I could even afford to treat myself to the Catalonian cooking course on top. Can you think of anyone who would book for us?"

"Wait a second," said Isy **tentatively**, thinking of a man who'd spent the last few months sitting on the beautiful, warm island of Malta working on his new book. She reached for her friend's mobile

---

as miserable as sin – wie sieben Tage Regenwetter;
I couldn't give a toss – es ist mir schnurzegal;
tentatively – zögerlich

phone and dialled a number while Amanda **glued** her blue eyes to her. "Who is it?"

"The man who's always helped us out."

"The mythical man? But he's..."

"Maybe he's back already."

"Hi!" cried Isy, as she heard the pleasant male voice in her ear. "It's great you're back! It's me and Amanda, your two best friends! Unfortunately we've got another slight problem, and you always said we were like daughters to you..."

"Two **pretty impossible** daughters," sighed the man. "What's the trouble now?"

Two weeks later they were on their way to the traditional hotel, the Forest View Inn. A medium-sized, grey dog was **snoring** between them on the back seat of the burgundy Golf. The afternoon sun was making his **fur** shine.

At the steering wheel sat the famous **thriller writer** Patrick Mortimer Rimpau.

Isy was proud they'd been able to **talk him into** this. She and Amanda had met the writer and his dog two years ago in their **school's country lodge**

---

to glue – heften, kleben; pretty impossible – ziemlich unmöglich; to snore – schnarchen; fur – Fell;
thriller writer – Krimiautor; to talk sb into sth – jmdn. zu etwas überreden; school's country lodge – Schullandheim

in Green Meadows. They'd initially suspected the writer of having robbed the post office, but soon things were cleared up, and fortunately Mr Rimpau hadn't been too angry with them at the time.

Since then he'd been their **guardian angel** on more than one occasion, helping them out of tricky situations during their **investigative** adventures. One could almost say Isy and Amanda trusted him as much as they trusted each other, and that he'd become their friend.

"I'll end up in **jail** because of you two," he mumbled just then. "Mature writer in his forties kidnaps **underage** adventurers under the **pretext** of a school trip to the Erz traditional hotel, the Forest View Inn."

"It is a school trip," giggles Amanda. "Isy and I are in the same class anyway."

"I suspect class trips have a somewhat different definition." The writer **overtook** a series of **lorries**. "If you'd just give me an honest answer about what you want to do there!"

"Attend courses," came two voices quickly from the back seat.

"In carving?" asked the writer sceptically. "In lacemaking? In playing the zither or baking Hutzen cake? That doesn't exactly fit your characters!"

---

guardian angel – Schutzengel; investigative – detektivisch; jail – Knast; underage – minderjährig; pretext – Vorwand; to overtake – überholen; lorry – Lastwagen

"We thought it would be good to try something different," said Isy.

"Tradition is back in fashion," said Amanda.

The writer said nothing. He'd known the calamity queens long enough. Concentrating on the road, he steered through the **rolling meadows** and corn fields. On the horizon an **undulating** skyline announced the oncoming mountains.

An hour later the Golf pulled up in front of a villa with **turrets** and a grey **slate** roof.

"Voilà, Mademoiselles! We're here. From now on I'm your new dad. Is that clear?"

"Perfectly clear," they cried. Then they jumped out of the car and embraced. They'd made it!

"A **lofty** castle," mumbled Amanda with a look of **acknowledgement** as she **scrutinised** the hotel.

In the meantime Mr Rimpau carried the luggage into the Forest View Inn and checked in for them.

When the two friends finally turned up in the foyer with the beautiful, carved pyramids, the writer was already waving the room key at them. They went up the stairs on gently creaking steps and disappeared into their pretty room which contained two carved beds, a matching **wardrobe** and

---

rolling meadows – ausgedehnte Weiden;
undulating – gewölbt, gewellt; turrets – Türmchen;
slate – Schiefer; lofty – erhaben;
acknowledgement – Anerkennung; to scrutinise – mustern

a table with two chairs in front of the window which framed the promised forest view.

"This is the life!" declared Amanda, throwing herself with a **clatter** onto the bed.

Now Mr Rimpau could go.

As if Patrick Mortimer Rimpau could read their minds he turned towards the door. "Oh, by the way, I'm in the next room. Here's to us being neighbours!"

The girls exchanged a look of **confusion**.

"Don't you..." Isy stuttered. "Don't you have to go home to your book, Dad?"

"I brought everything with me," the writer raised a bag into the air grinning. "That's what laptops are for. Have I ever **left** you two **in the lurch** before? See you at dinner."

They watched him go with long faces. That was a surprise! A male **nanny** is all they needed!

Although Amanda claimed that the writer's decision to spend the week with them in the Forest View Inn had ruined her appetite, it didn't seem to stop her from **tucking** hungrily **into** her dinner. While Amanda ate, Isy kept an **inconspicuous** look out for young men with black hair.

---

wardrobe – Kleiderschrank; clatter – Krach;
confusion – Verwirrung;
to leave sb in the lurch – jmdn. im Stich lassen;
nanny – Kindermädchen; to tuck into – kräftig zulangen;
inconspicuous – unauffällig

"So? Have you spotted one yet?" whispered Amanda before she attacked the buffet for a third time with her empty plate. "And don't forget to eat."

"She's right! Don't forget to eat," a young man with black curly hair and equally black eyes whispered into her ear as he filled up Mr Rimpau's glass of red wine. "Or shall I bring you something else?"

"Thank you, but my daughter's about to go to the buffet with me," said the writer kindly as he pulled Isy up from her chair.

That's a good start, thought Isy as she **furtively** exchanged glances with the young waiter. She followed the writer over to the tasty salads with a sigh.

After about an hour the writer retired to his laptop. **Beforehand,** however, he made sure he brought the two girls back to their room where he reminded them about the morning gymnastics. In doing so he seemed to be addressing Amanda in particular.

"I expect you're both tired now," he said to bring the evening to a close. "Sleep well!"

He'd only just gone out when Amanda started **tearing her hair out**. "What a disaster! Morning gymnastics? We've got to get out of that. We're being **guarded tighter** than the gold in Fort Knox. He's... he's even capable of locking us up!"

---

furtively – insgeheim; beforehand – vorher;
to tear the hair out – sich die Haare ausraufen;
to guard tight – streng bewachen

"I hope not," sighed Isy. "Then neither of us will be able to get out..."

"And no one will be able to get *in* either!" exclaimed Amanda, lighting a cigarette. She always liked to have a puff just to look good and make sure the air was bad.

They heard a dog barking at the top of its voice outside in the grounds. Isy peered through the curtains to look for Alfredo, but the grounds were covered in an evening **mist**, and it was almost impossible to see anything. She could only just make out the faint silhouette of a large, black dog. "Mr Rimpau means well," she said in a slightly apologetic tone.

"That's the problem," snorted Amanda. Then she tilted her head to one side **expectantly**. "By the way, have you spotted one already?"

"Yep. A really **cute guy**!" Isy immediately knew what Amanda was talking about. "He served our table when you were at the buffet."

"Did he try to **chat** you **up**?"

"I think so."

"I only saw men with grey hair," moaned Amanda. "It's scandalous!" She disappeared into the bathroom and came out again in her best **nightie**. Just to be on the safe side she opened the window wide open.

---

mist – Nebel; expectantly – erwartungsvoll; cute guy – süßer Typ; to chat up – anmachen; nightie – Nachthemd

"Leave it closed! I don't think he'll be coming tonight. We've only just got here..."

"I think he will," disagreed Amanda as she opened the window even wider. "Perhaps your cute waiter will **climb in through his lover's window** tonight?"

Whatever next, Amanda! She could hardly wait! Isy pulled the covers up under her chin with a grin. They'd stay awake just to be on the safe side: Amanda for the first half of the night, Isy for the second. That was the plan.

"Sleep well. I'll wake you up when he gets here," assured Amanda. "Only after he's kissed me of course." She rolled onto her side, then onto the other side, and in less than a minute she was fast asleep.

Isy was **dumbfounded** to hear the first gentle snores from Amanda's bed. That's not what we'd agreed on, she thought angrily. She was meant to stay awake first, then me, then...

But before she was able to think through the plan, she also drifted off into the **realm** of dreams.

The next morning they both woke up for gymnastics at seven **on the dot**. Unkissed.

---

to climb in through his lover's window – fensterln; dumbfounded – entgeistert; realm – Reich, Königreich; on the dot – auf den Punkt genau

At breakfast the two **grumpy** girls hid their disappointed faces behind their bowls of muesli and large cups of hot chocolate.

Mr Rimpau couldn't help noticing them anyway. He **frowned anxiously**. "Get out of bed on the wrong side?"

"It's just because... Amanda **messed it** all **up**!" muttered Isy irately.

"That's not true!" denied Amanda.

Then they fell back into an icy silence.

The writer tried to find some meaning in the reply, but **to no avail**. He soon gave up and went to plunder the bread basket.

"How can I help it if I fell asleep?" grumbled Amanda. Then she said, "You could have stayed awake and woken me up at half-time!"

"Ha! Now it's my fault?" **snorted** Isy, but Amanda was right. The truth was Isy was annoyed with herself. "I bet he never came anyway. Besides, we still have five more whole nights."

"Is that all?!" **whined** Amanda. "I'm **dying to** fall in love."

As if on **cue** a sporty, sun-tanned boy with bright blue eyes appeared in the breakfast room. He was

---

grumpy – muffig, mürrisch;
to frown anxiously – besorgt die Stirn runzeln;
to mess sth up – etwas verpatzen; to no avail – vergebens;
to snort – schnauben; to whine – jammern;
to die to – etwas unbedingt wollen; cue – Stichwort

wearing white jeans and was carrying a basket full of fresh bread. He glanced at the two girls inquisitively.

"Oh, he's cute!" stuttered Amanda longingly.

"But his hair isn't really black," commented Isy critically. "More dark blonde."

"Don't you think that... er... Jennifer Niemann is sometimes a bit colour blind?"

Before Isy could reply, Mr Rimpau was back at the table.

"So tell me, were you staring greedily at the fresh bread or the **handsome** waiter carrying it?" he asked cheerfully.

They continued chewing with reddened faces and were grateful when an elderly lady broke the embarrassed silence. She had recognised her favourite writer and quickly asked Mr Rimpau for an **autograph**. The writer kindly fulfilled her wish.

Then it was time for the courses. Isy disappeared towards the music room, Amanda to the hotel kitchen, and Mr Rimpau went down to the cellar. He'd signed up for the carving workshop.

In the afternoon the girls strolled through the park with Alfredo. Isy could already play the first few bars of "Come dear May and make..." on the instrument that she'd never touched until that

---

handsome – gut aussehend; autograph – Autogramm

morning – the zither – and Amanda had got to know some of the local specialities. The plan was to bake a Hutzen cake at the end of the course and take it home with her.

In the meantime Mr Rimpau had acquired a big, fat **thumb** which was wrapped in a **bandage**. If he'd learnt one thing that morning, it was that a man should **stick to his trade**. That's why he was now back at his laptop.

Isy and Amanda, however, were looking for love.

Love had black hair, was cheeky and **bold**, and kissed pretty girls secretly at night. But where the devil was he **hiding**?

A lot of boys crossed their path and were sniffed at by Alfredo with his wagging tail: young and old, fat and thin, blonde and red-haired – but **Mr Right** wasn't amongst them. If only the cute, curly black-haired waiter or the **gorgeous** guy from this morning would turn up, thought Isy with a slight sense of desperation. But not a chance! Disheartened, she dropped down onto a park bench.

The scent of roses drifted over from the bushes. English roses, as Mr Rimpau had told them.

---

thumb – Daumen; bandage – Verband;
stick to his trade – sinngemäß: bei seinen Leisten bleiben (Schuster); bold – kühn; to hide – sich verstecken;
Mr Right – der Richtige;
gorgeous – umwerfend, atemberaubend

"Maybe Jennifer really did imagine it all," muttered Amanda.

"Er, I don't think so. There's something in the air here," sniffed Isy ominously. "As if... as if something unbelievable... could happen any second!"

Just then something unbelievable did indeed happen. The boy with the bright blue eyes came strolling **nonchalantly** over the **lawn**. He was walking a large, black-haired Newfoundland dog. "Is yours male?" he called. "Then put him on a lead."

They put Alfredo on the lead and waited for the blue-eyed boy to get closer.

Amanda gave him her most charming smile. "I'm Amanda and this is my friend, Isolde."

"Timo...Is that your dog?"

Amanda shook her head. "Alfredo belongs to Mr Rimpau."

"The writer? Isn't he your dad?"

Amanda jumped and the blood rushed to her face. She looked at Isy helplessly.

"Our dad loves it when we call him Mr Rimpau," Isy improvised to save the situation.

"Dads are strange, aren't they? I always call mine *boss*."

"Does he always **pretend** to play the boss?"

"Not exactly, but he owns the hotel and the park."

---

nonchalantly – lässig; lawn – Rasen;
to pretend – so tun als ob

"Well, I never!" exclaimed Amanda, scrutinising him with interest. "So you'll be a rich **heir** then?"

"It only looks like that. I've got four brothers."

"So is the waiter with the black curly hair your brother as well?" As she asked this question, Isy's heart started racing out of control.

"You're thinking of Peer. Everybody in my family works in the hotel. He's still learning."

The dogs sniffed each other, their **legs cocked**.

So he's called Peer. Isy stroked the Newfoundland dog. "Good-looking guy!"

Timo looked at his watch. "Lord has to go to the **vet**. His **sedative injection**."

"Is he ill?"

"No, he's just a bit... in **need of affection**."

"By the way," sighed Amanda. "We're in room 3."

"Room 3? So the two of you aren't **superstitious** then?" Timo grinned. "See you around!"

"See you around!" replied the girls in **unison**.

"By the way," said Isy, imitating her friend just after Timo had gone, "we're in room 3... That was really **subtle**!"

"What's your problem? That's why we're here!"

"But what if it isn't him? I mean, he's dark blonde."

---

heir – Erbe; legs cocked – steifbeinig; vet – Tierarzt; sedative injection – Beruhigungsspritze;
in need of affection – liebesbedürftig;
superstitious – abergläubisch; in unison – einstimmig;
subtle – subtil

"You just want Peer to be the kissing stranger!" Amanda leaned over the park bench **confidentially**. "Though I can't really see why it's particularly **worth striving** to be kissed by the same guy as Jennifer Niemann."

"Me, neither."

"I mean, she's no competition."

"You said it," confirmed Isy. "But do we have any other choice?"

Not if we want to catch him, we don't, thought Isy. And there's nothing more they wanted to do than catch the kissing stranger. Her detective's sense of **ambition** had **caught alight**. Amanda could go on pretending to be romantic if she wanted!

But that night the two girls were disappointed again. No stranger's cheek **snuggled up** to them. No stranger's lips gently touched theirs. Despite the fact that they'd spent half the night lying awake and pricking up their ears at even the faintest sound, love had once again **eluded** them.

"And I even told him our room number," said Amanda, **incensed**. She checked the door distrust-

---

confidentially – vertraulich; worth striving – erstrebenswert;
ambition caught alight – Ehrgeiz entfacht;
to snuggle up – sich anschmiegen;
to elude – aus dem Weg gehen; incensed – erzürnt

fully, but it had been open all night. The two **casement windows** as well.

They seemed to be doing something wrong. But what?

"It's our neighbour," hissed Amanda. "Mr Rimpau is **scaring** him **off**!"

"Mr Rimpau sleeps **like a log**," corrected Isy. The writer assured them of this fact every morning.

No, it had to be something else. But what?

After an hour's practise on the chirping zither, **the scales** suddenly **fell from her eyes**. She impatiently left the course and burst into the hotel kitchen. There – instead of rolling Sushi in Tokyo as she'd originally wanted – Amanda was squeezing hot potatoes through a press to make Saxon *fromage frais* with a group of **like-minded** people.

"I've got it! I know what the problem is."

"So? What is the problem? Enlighten me!"

"It's the room," declared Isy. "Jennifer said she stayed in room 7. We have to move to room 7!"

"Do you really think so?" Amanda hesitated for a moment. Then she undid her **apron** and followed her friend to reception.

"I'm terribly sorry," said the lady at reception. "Room 7 is occupied."

---

casement windows – Fensterflügel;
to scare sb off – jmdn. verscheuchen;
to sleep like a log – wie ein Stein schlafen;
the scales fall from sb's eyes – jmdm. fällt es wie Schuppen von den Augen; like-minded – gleichgesinnt; apron – Schürze

"Is there nothing you can do?" asked Isy. "My friend suffers from... **vertigo**. She feels sick when she looks out of the window. Even on the first floor."

Amanda nodded, drowning in **self-pity**. "It's really bad."

"I'm afraid there's nothing we can do," apologized the hotel woman. "The woman in Room 7 always asks explicitly for the same room. Oh, there she is."

That's a bit of luck, thought Isy as she went to **introduce herself** to the lady.

Five minutes later they were changing their rooms.

Amanda's eyes were the size of two XXL fried eggs. "How did you manage that?" she asked in amazement as they packed away their things in the blue stained wardrobe of Room 7.

"Easy. I told her we were Mr Rimpau's daughters. She was that woman who wanted an autograph from him yesterday morning. It was **a piece of cake**. Now she can sleep wall to wall with her favourite writer – and we've got Room 7!"

"And what are we going to tell Mr Rimpau?"

Isy had been waiting for that question. She twisted her mouth into a **mischievous** smile. "The same

---

vertigo – Höhenangst; self-pity – Selbstmitleid;
to introduce oneself – sich vorstellen;
a piece of cake – hier: ein Kinderspiel;
mischievous – schelmisch, spitzbübisch

thing I told the woman from Room 7, of course: that he snores **atrociously** when he sleeps like a log!"

"What makes you think I snore?" cried the writer **indignantly**, as he surprised them that afternoon with a drive through the Erz Mountains. "No one's ever said that before. And why do you want to sleep in Room 7?"

"Oh, it's nice and close to the lawn," said Isy.

"Oh, you don't have to go up any stairs," said Amanda.

The writer said nothing. He'd known the calamity queens long enough.

The Golf **purred** through the valleys where the villages clung to the green mountain **slopes** like colourful toy houses. They crossed glistening rivers and passed dark forests whose edges were lined with tall **spruces** and **rowans** with red fruits. What the ancient Romans had once called Miriquidi, the dark forest, was in fact a friendly place with friendly people who patiently carved marvellous pyramids, candlesticks or model trees and hordes of funny little carved figures for themselves and the rest of the world.

"And if you come back right at the beginning of winter," explained the writer enthusiastically, "then

---

atrociously – ganz entsetzlich; indignantly – entrüstet;
to purr – schnurren; slope – Hang; spruce – Fichte;
rowan – Eberesche

you'll be amazed to see the transformation of the **lush** Erz Mountains into Germany's most beautiful, most glorious and most sparkling Christmas land."

They had a foretaste of this as they strolled through the famous Seiffner toy museum. Then they drank a coffee with Mr Rimpau at the foot of the Fichtel mountains, and in Annaberg, the heart of the former silver mine, they visited the **memorial home** of the master of arithmetic, Adam Ries.

"Him of all people!" groaned Amanda, who thought maths was a nightmare. But she **stuck it out**.

At dinner that evening they all had a lot to talk about, but it didn't stop the girls from bombarding black-haired Peer at the buffet with **fervent** looks. Graced by his gentle smile, Isy bravely went for three portions of the onion soup which she didn't even like. Amanda on the other hand whispered furtively over dishes of fragrant cheese to him, telling him to let Timo know that they'd moved into Room 7.

They left in the confidence that everything had been prepared for the coming night and went straight to bed. And between midnight and sunrise it finally happened: they were kissed!

At some point in the middle of the night, while still half asleep, they felt a wave of warmth, **tender-**

---

lush – saftig grün; memorial home – Gedenkhaus;
to stick it out – durchhalten; fervent – schwärmerisch;
tenderness and intimacy – Zärtlichkeit und Nähe

ness and intimacy as their hands touched a pair of broad shoulders and full, soft hair. It was like being in a wonderful dream. But they were woken up abruptly when a door banged somewhere in the hotel.

"Amanda, wake up!" whispered Isy. "He was here!" She rushed over to the door, **slightly stunned**, and peered into the corridor. It was empty. And through the open window she could see nothing more than the dark summer's night which smelt of grass.

"I think someone just... kissed me," murmured Amanda, still half asleep.

"Me, too! Me, too!" cried Isy for joy. "At first I thought it was just a dream..."

For a moment there was a dreamy silence in Room 7.

Then Isy **spluttered**. "What on earth do you look like?!"

Amanda's lipstick was smeared over her face, and there was a black hair stuck to the end of her nose! It was the ultimate **proof** for the kissing stranger's visit. The plan with Room 7 had worked! Jennifer Niemann had been telling the truth.

They examined the hair in the light of the bed-side table, their fingers trembling. Amanda claimed it was dark blonde. Isy said it was black.

---

slightly stunned – leicht benommen;
to splutter – herausplatzen; proof – Beweis

"It was Timo," declared Amanda decisively after her morning gymnastics. "I can feel it."

"It was Peer," disagreed Isy, whose hands had touched those of Peer three times as she went to get more onion soup. Her painful **stomach cramp** after the soup was nothing in comparison with her sudden feeling of happiness.

"What's going on here then? You two are **smiling your heads off**," Mr Rimpau commented with pleasure at breakfast as he put a **recording device** next to the fruit jam. "Now listen to this."

For a while they did him the favour and made an effort to listen, but they couldn't make out the slightest sound.

"Can you hear anything?"

They shook their heads.

Mr Rimpau turned the device on to full volume. "Can you hear anything now?"

"No," said Amanda.

"Not a thing," said Isy.

"That's a recording of my snoring throughout the whole of last night," said the writer proudly.

He'd **caught them out**!

---

stomach cramp – Magenkrampf;
to smile the head off – vor Freude strahlen;
recording device – Aufnahmegerät;
to catch sb out – jmdn. austricksen

Humiliated, the two girls slipped off to their courses.

In the afternoon they wrote postcards home to their parents, their grandmothers and their favourite aunts. *All the best from our school trip!* they scribbled on the back of romantic picture postcards showing the photogenic traditional hotel. Now and again a **quiet sigh** fell from their lips. This could have been **translated** as *I hope they never find out about this*!

After that they went to the pool. There were a number of blonde, red and black-haired boys **prancing around**, but Timo and Peer were nowhere to be seen. They were probably busy in the hotel.

"Those were the most passionate kisses I've ever had," sighed Amanda, melting as she sweltered in the sun on the sunbathing lawn.

"Have you kissed a lot then?" asked Isy sceptically.

"Sure," claimed Amanda, but she was glad the thickly spread sun cream hid the bright red **embarrassment** on her cheeks. Isy didn't have to know that boys had only ever kissed her on the forehead until now.

---

humiliated – beschämt; quiet sigh – leiser Seufzer;
to translate – übersetzen;
to prancing around – herumstolzieren;
embarrassment – Verlegenheit

"Yes, the kisses were **above average**," agreed Isy, desperately hoping that Amanda would never find out that it was her first kiss. Besides she hadn't exactly got a lot from the whole procedure, her being half sleep at the time …

For a while they were lost in their non-existent memories. Then Isy buried herself in an exciting teenage novel, while Amanda leafed through her magazines, hungry for gossip. And when the sun took its leave of the swimming pool with a cool smile, they also went back to the hotel.

They were still **preoccupied** with the burning question of the night-time visitor's identity. But in the course of the day, as the fresh morning **sluggishly** changed into a mild evening, so too did their bold conviction that last night it could only be *one* boy gradually changed into the wish that it might be better if it wasn't the chosen boy at all. Yes, it was certainly **strange** what was happening to them all of a sudden!

If it was Timo, he'd better watch it, or **he'll have me to deal with**, thought Amanda angrily. I'll certainly put a stop to him kissing my best friend!

If it was Peer, then he needs **glasses**! thought Isy,

---

above average – überdurchschnittlich;
preoccupied – vertieft; sluggishly – träge;
strange – hier: seltsam;
he'll have me to deal with – er bekommt es mit mir zu tun;
glasses – Brille

no less unhappy about the idea. It's a sign of real bad taste to **mix** me **up** with Amanda Bornstein!

They went to their room without saying a word. As they unpacked their swimming bags, they both knew that their **pride** could only be saved if they found out the truth.

"You're both so quiet," probed Mr Rimpau at dinner. "Did you have an argument?"

The girls shook their heads emphatically.

"Then we could play a round of **rummy** after dinner if you want?"

"Yeah, sure!" they mumbled as if with one voice.

The writer got to his feet, a satisfied expression on his face, and went to get another portion of roast potatoes while Isy **bashfully** wrapped a piece of **lettuce** around her fork. "By the way, last night," she began hesitantly, "I don't think... it was Peer. The hair was more dark blonde than black. You were right."

"And I don't think it was Timo!" Amanda replied quickly. "As far as the colour of the hair's concerned – it all depends on the light. **Unreliable** evidence!"

"Then we're agreed," said Isy, surprised.

"Yes, but..."

---

to mix up – verwechseln; pride – Stolz; rummy – Rommee; bashfully – verschämt; lettuce – Salat; unreliable – unzuverlässig

"Exactly. We have to know for sure!"

"You said it! Have you got an idea?"

"Not yet..."

They smiled at each other over their salad bowls with a sense of **relief**. They always ended up thinking the same thing. Well, nearly always.

Isy came up with an idea after they'd survived three rounds of rummy with Mr Rimpau and the door to their room finally closed behind them. "I know how to find out. We have to... we have to set him a **trap**!"

"And how do you intend to do that?" said Amanda as she swung her blouse over her head.

"Who said *I'm* going to do it? *You're* going to do it!" Isy giggled as she saw Amanda's wide open eyes. "Unfortunately, you've got to spend the night in the wardrobe."

The plan was brilliant. After watching night-time TV for a bit, Amanda would move into the light blue wardrobe with some cushions and a **duvet**.

"What if I **suffocate**?" she protested.

"We'll leave the door open a **fraction**."

"Why don't you do it yourself?"

"I grew too much last year."

"Really?" Amanda eyed up her friend sceptical-

---

relief – Erleichterung; trap – Falle;
duvet – Bettdecke;
to suffocate – ersticken; fraction – Spalt

ly, but it was true. Isy had shot up like an **asparagus** and was now at least five centimetres taller than her. "But you're a lot thinner than I am!"

"It's not about the **width**, it's the height. I'd have to tie a knot in my legs."

"And how am I meant to sleep? Standing up?" asked Amanda.

"Don't you dare! You shouldn't sleep at all. Otherwise you won't be able to see who kisses me."

"I won't be able to see anyway. I'm not an **owl** who can see in the dark!"

"Oh, come on, you'll at least be able to make out a shadow! And then you can quickly jump out of the wardrobe and turn on the light..."

"Out of the wardrobe? In the dark? That's a mega-stupid idea!"

"You can think it's stupid if you want," defended Isy. "But do you want to find out if it's really your Timo or not?"

Amanda wanted to find out just that.

After the last movie they emptied their things out of the wardrobe, and Amanda transferred her bed covers with a sigh. For a while Isy heard her friend **tinkering around** inside the wardrobe, and then it creaked one last time behind the wooden door. The night could come!

---

asparagus – Spargel; width – Breite; owl – Eule;
to tinker around – herumkruschteln

The night came and sleeping was completely out of the question. Isy **tossed** and turned restlessly. Would he come? Would the trap work? And, above all, who would he be? Timo or Peer? Or perhaps even… somebody else?

"I'm twisted up like a **corkscrew** in here!" complained Amanda from inside the wardrobe. "My left leg has gone to sleep."

"The main thing is you don't go to sleep!" Those were the last words Isy could remember. Then Morpheus, the Greek god of sleep, gently took her in his arms until the broad stranger snuggled up to her in the early hours of the morning, full of warmth and intimacy, his hair soft and his kisses moist. *Amanda…* thought Isy in the gentle turmoils of her light sleep, *Amanda, he's there, be careful…*

By the time she'd finally shaken off the last crumbs of sleep, she was alone. The only movement came from the curtains at the open window which were blowing as a gentle **farewell** in the wind. But inside the blue wardrobe someone was snoring loudly!

"That's **outrageous**! He was here, and you slept through it like a log!"

---

to toss – werfen; corkscrew – Korkenzieher;
farewell – Abschiedsgruß; outrageous – ungeheuerlich

"Do you know who it was?" asked Amanda.

"Ha! *You* were meant to find that out!"

"Sorry! But you try spending the whole night in the wardrobe!"

"Anyway, I felt a… tongue…"

"You felt his tongue?" squeaked Amanda **delighted**.

"Yes… no… I don't know. He always comes when I'm fast asleep!"

"Who does your **gut feeling** say it was? Timo or Peer?"

"Timo maybe…"

"That's not true! You've got no proof!" shrieked Amanda.

That was true. She had no proof. Besides, she'd only said it because she was angry with her friend. Isy lowered her eyes, ashamed.

In the meantime Amanda had squeezed into her pink **tracksuit**.

"Have you put on a bit of weight with all the good food?"

"Quite the opposite! I've lost weight!" replied Amanda **snottily**. "And just so you know: if Timo kissed you last night, he can **go take a running jump** as far as I'm concerned!"

---

delighted – entzückt; gut feeling – Intuition;
tracksuit – Gymnastikanzug; snottily – patzig;
sb can go take a running jump – jmd. kann einem gestohlen bleiben

"And if Peer kissed you, he can take a running jump as well!"

Mr Rimpau was surprised to pick up the bad atmosphere again at breakfast. The girls only opened their mouths to put something **edible** in. "How are your courses going?" he asked to try and **lift their spirits**.

They shrugged their shoulders without saying a word. They were pretending to be cool, but in reality they were keeping an eye out for Timo and Peer with **quivering** hearts. But the bread was brought in by someone else today. Also a boy with black hair. Maybe brother number three?

"Thanks a lot, you've been great company," said Mr Rimpau as they disappeared off to their courses without saying a word.

Amanda was surprised to see Isy follow her into the hotel kitchen. "Bored of your **mountain banjo**?"

"Not at all. I just need a packet of **flour** from your cooking course."

"What for?"

"You'll see!" Isy didn't say another word, **leaving** Amanda **on tenterhooks** the whole day long.

Then the long awaited evening finally came, and Isy began to open the mysterious packet of flour.

---

edible – essbar; to lift sb's spirits – jmdn. aufmuntern;
to quiver – beben, zittern; mountain banjo – Gebirgsklampfe;
flour – Mehl; to leave sb on tenterhooks – jmdn. auf die Folter spannen

Amanda, who was smoking on her bed, watched her with interest. Isy first **scattered** half the packet of flour **liberally** in front of the bedroom door. Then she did the same in front of the window. By the time the packet was empty, Amanda was in the grip of a **sneezing fit**.

"Scattering grain through the room? Is that some witches' ritual or are you **off your rocker**?"

"I hope the footprints in the flour will open your eyes tomorrow morning! What did that poet say?" Isy chuckled. "*You shall recognise them by their feet*! Or something like that... Whoever he is, he'll have to walk through our flour trap with his **clodhoppers**, whether he comes through the door or jumps in through the window."

"You're not going to steal Timo and Peer's shoes tomorrow?" asked Amanda aghast.

"Why not?" yawned Isy. "You want proof!"

"It's **just as well** there are only two possibilities."

"You mean three."

"Why three?"

"Don't forget the broad stranger! That's why we're here. If it's not Timo or Peer, then it's a third per-

---

to scatter – verstreuen; liberally – absichtlich;
sneezing fit – Niesanfall;
to be off the rocker – nicht mehr alle Tassen im Schrank haben; clodhopper – Quadratlatschen
just as well – nur gut, ein Glück

son, and we have exactly two nights to find out who!"

"And what would you say if it was... the gardener for instance?"

"Well, **on that note: goodnight**, Amanda!"

In the last phase of deep sleep Amanda dreamed of a **deep sea dive** into a sea of blooming corals and brightly coloured fish, and Isy dreamed of a market square in an unknown town. She was just about to buy herself a beautiful red **necklace** when Amanda started breathlessly calling, "Wake up! Wake up! He was here!"

Stunned and still half asleep, Isy jumped out of bed and **staggered** over to the door where she bent over the flour. But apart from her own footprints, there was nothing new. Nor did the flour in front of the window reveal the stranger's footsteps. A glance at the **alarm clock** told her it was time to get up anyway. "Why do you think he was here?" she murmured. "Besides, it's almost seven o'clock!"

"Here's why!" Amanda opened her clenched fist.

In the palm of her hand Isy counted three shiny black hairs. They couldn't believe their eyes!

---

on that note: goodnight – na dann gute Nacht;
deep sea dive – Tiefseetauchen; necklace – Halskette;
to stagger – stolpern, taumeln; alarm clock – Wecker

"All three were on my pillow!" announced Amanda triumphantly. "And as far as I can remember, I'm blonde."

Perplexed, Isy let her gaze wander over the untouched flour in front of the window and door. "If he really was in our room, then he must be able to fly! Or he was an Olympic gold medallist in the **long jump** ..." Disappointed, she slung her morning gymnastics towel over her shoulder and followed Amanda onto the lawn. The guy was just too smart to catch! It was hardly surprising that **naïve** young Jennifer Niemann never managed to unmask the kissing stranger, but two **tough** girls like Amanda and her? It pricked Isy's self-confidence so badly that it actually hurt. She'd probably never solve the mystery of this Kissing Crime! As a detective used to success, she'd failed for the first time...

It was only when she saw Timo smiling bashfully that her mood picked up. He was waiting for them in the park with his magnificent dog Lord and two invitations to the farewell disco. While Amanda turned as red as a **hibiscus bloom**, Isy was **thrilled** to accept the invitation. At last something positive!

But there were a few more things to be done before (much to their amazement) they'd see Mr Rimpau swinging his hotel neighbour over his shoulder

---

long jump – Weitsprung; naïve – einfältig; tough – zäh; hibiscus bloom – Hibiskusblüte; thrilled – begeistert

while dancing rock 'n' roll in the late hours of the evening: Isy had to try and pluck all of the pieces she'd learned on the zither without making a mistake, and Amanda had to bake a Hutzen cake to end her cooking course. They also went to buy some souvenirs for their loved ones at home in the little shops in the old town. After all that they could finally **let their hair down** at the farewell party.

Oh, that night could have gone on for ever! The looks from Timo and Peer. The scent of the English roses. The last dance. The fireworks in the park. That tingling **spark**. The first kiss!

Around midnight they were lying happily in bed. And both of them had been kissed! Amanda by Timo, Isy by Peer. Their dream had come true.

"Even so! I'd still like to know who it was!" **insisted** Isy wearily.

"Who cares?" protested Amanda. "Nobody's going to come tonight. Not even the gardener..."

"He won't come anyway. I saw him this morning. He's bald," explained Isy. "The only other person who comes into question is the cook. But he always wears his white hat," she snorted.

---

to let the hair down – sich gehen lassen, ausgelassen sein; spark – Funke; to insist – beharren

"I think you should finally send your ambitions to be a detective to sleep," yawned Amanda. "Miss **Deputy Chief Inspector**!"

"Miss **Chief Commissioner**, if you please," Isy corrected her friend, but she didn't get an answer. Amanda had already drifted off into Morpheus' realm.

So much the better, thought Isy, and when she heard her friend start snoring, she slipped out of bed and hid underneath it. Phew! It was **dusty**! Her nose immediately began to twitch, but she pulled herself together. This was her last chance! But did she really still want to find out the truth? Even if it was Peer?

Yes, she wanted to know!

For a while she listened to the slowly subsiding sounds in the hotel. Then the place finally fell silent, and her feet started to get cold. After half an eternity she decided to give up and **was just about to** creep back into bed with **aching calves** when she heard a loud **thump**. Now all she had to do was take a good look at the feet! That evening Timo had been wearing white Nike sneakers and Peer black ones from Reebok.

Deputy Chief Inspector – Ober-Unterinspektor;
Chief Commissioner – Hauptkommissar; dusty – staubig;
to be just about to – gerade etwas tun wollen;
aching calves – schmerzende Waden;
thump – dumpfer Knall

Her heart was pounding, her pulse was racing, and the dust was tickling her nose like crazy. And all of a sudden, she had to sneeze. For a fleeting moment the night-time visitor seemed to freeze. Then he ran out of the window and escaped into the park.

This couldn't be true! **Utterly bewildered**, Isy crawled out from underneath the bed and could only see a dark shadow disappearing between the trees. Damn and blast! She'd been so close!

The next morning she was sitting in the burgundy Golf with Amanda. Alfredo was snoring between them on the back seat. With a slightly **melancholic** heart they left the friendly Miriquidi region. They could smell the Hutzen cake in the trunk. The previous night's uncrowned king of rock 'n' roll – the famous thriller writer, Patrick Mortimer Rimpau – **sat enthroned** at the steering wheel.

"You can dance so well!" sighed Amanda, full of admiration. Then she fell silent again.

Amanda was thinking about Timo, and Isy about Peer.

"What did you two think of the week?" asked the writer as he turned onto the motorway. "Did it fulfil your **expectations**?"

---

utterly bewildered – völlig fassungslos;
melancholic – wehmütig; to sit enthroned – thronen;
expectations – Erwartungen

"More or less," mumbled Amanda mysteriously.

"Both **the former and the latter**," mumbled Isy even more mysteriously.

Their attempt to avoid answering the question didn't go unnoticed by the writer. He tossed a newspaper chirpily onto the back seat. "I took the local paper with me from the hotel. Have a look at page four!"

They opened the newspaper. On page four someone had marked an article with a cross. It was called *Tales from the Animal World!*

"You read it," said Amanda, and she turned her attention to writing Timo a **slushy** SMS.

"The guests of the well-known traditional hotel, the Forest View Inn, can finally breathe a sigh of relief," Isy read quietly. *"The mystery of Room 7 has been solved at last! Visitors to this ground-floor room in the summer months repeatedly complained that they were visited by a stranger who snuggled up to them and smothered them with tender kisses during the night. On the basis of a precise scientific analysis of the black hairs found at the scene of the crime, it has since been proved that the nightly visitor was none other than the hotel's black Newfoundland dog Lord. The hotel management informed us that the dog is currently undergoing medical treatment to resolve his excessive need of affection..."* At this point Isy's voice

---

the former and the latter – sowohl als auch;
slushy – schmachtend, verliebt;
to smother – hier: bedecken

trailed off. No wonder there were no footprints in the flour. The kissing stranger was none other than the **huge** dog Lord!

For a while everything was so still in the car that Mr Rimpau kept glancing anxiously into the rear-view mirror. "What's the matter?" he asked with a grin. "Why have you turned green all of a sudden?"

"It's the light!" said Amanda.

"I hope you're not getting **glaucoma**!" said Isy to Mr Rimpau.

The writer said nothing. He'd known the calamity queens long enough.

All the girls in 7b had fallen in love that summer! Saskia and Binette with their Basque **diving instructor**, Lola with a young fisherman from Corsica, and Rose with a **flautist** from Hungary. Lisa with a **stable hand** from Lüneburg, Sophie with her cousin from Halle, and Henriette with a high-school student from Florida. Jennifer Niemann had fallen in love with a Norwegian **trainee salmon breeder**, and Isy and Amanda with Timo and Peer.

This time they could also tell a tale or two at break

---

to trail off – abbrechen; huge – riesengroß;
glaucoma – grüner Star;
diving instructor – Tauchlehrer; flautist – Flötist;
stable hand – Stallknecht;
trainee salmon breeder – Lachszüchter-Lehrling

time with a certain smile. Not everything of course.

"So how was it in the Forest View Inn?" whispered Jennifer **with bated breath** as she bit into her sandwich.

Sassi and Bini, Lisa, Lola, Rose, Henriette and Sophie also pricked up their ears. Had the calamity queens solved another crime?

"What Forest View Inn?" Isy and Amanda played stupid.

"I thought... er... because you both asked me so many questions before the holidays..." mumbled Jennifer **disappointed**. "For the survey from Allensbach."

"Do you still want to know who kissed you?" asked Isy with a grin.

"Don't tell me you found out?!"

"It was a piece of cake! But you have to keep it to yourself!" Then Isy whispered the truth into Jennifer Niemann's ear.

A few seconds later she strolled off like she was walking on clouds. What was a Norwegian trainee salmon breeder from Trondheim in comparison with a real Lord?

---

with bated breath – gespannt; disappointed – enttäuscht

Sissi Flegel

Kisses, Compasses & Candlelight

Markus Fiesel, the editor of our *Daily Messenger*, was to blame for everything.

He called me just after the **Whitsun** holidays. "Hello, Mimi, you work **freelance** for our youth page, don't you? And I heard you want to become the best **travel writer** ever, right? Good. I think I've got just the thing for you. It's not exactly risk-free. In fact it's rather adventurous and – well – a real **challenge**. But it's worth the first prize: one week in Sri Lanka, Bali or Cuba with a partner of your choice."

I was immediately **thrilled to bits**. "Not exactly risk-free ... adventurous," those are the kind of words I just can't **resist**.

"So what's it about, Markus?" I asked as coolly as possible.

"It's a kind of competition. You have to fly to Rome in the summer holidays, meet up with the other **participants**, and **head off** into the moun-

---

Whitsun – Pfingsten; freelance – freier Mitarbeiter;
travel writer – Reisejournalist; challenge – Herausforderung;
to be thrilled to bits – hin und weg sein; to resist – widerstehen;
participant – Teilnehmer; to head off – losziehen

tains. The next morning you pack your rucksack with food for three days, grab a map, compass and that brilliant **hiking** device which is connected to all the satellites and can tell you the coordinates of your position..."

"It's an electronic navigational aid. Global Positioning System it's called. GPS for short," she informed him briefly.

"You know everything, my girl! Anyway, you get all that, and then they drop you off somewhere in the mountains – and now comes **the exciting bit**: three days later you have to turn up at a specific place by a specific time. Preferably all **in one piece** and in good spirits. Whoever arrives first wins the prize. That's the most important thing. It's all sponsored by some well-known sports company who are trying to **promote** the new GPS device to our local hikers. There are a few minor details, like the fact that no one can be older than eighteen and that six people will be chosen from the best **applicants**..."

"Whaaat? Markus, what if five hundred people apply? How am I **meant to** get into the top six, huh?" I asked him, flabbergasted.

---

hiking – Wandern; the exciting bit – das Spannende daran;
in one piece – heil und unversehrt;
to promote – Werbung machen;
applicant – Bewerber;
to be meant to – etwas tun sollen

"I can deal with that, Mimi," replied Markus. "The point is this: we're interested in the report you could write about it. The way I know you, **you're bound to** write another big seller which will **boost** the sales of our *Daily Messenger*."

"Markus, don't **take the mickey**!"

"I'm not. I think highly of you, Mimi. Anyway, all I wanted to say is: if you send in your application with your best articles, nothing can go wrong!"

"The school magazine and the *Daily Messenger*?"

"Yeah, sure! I'll **cross my fingers** for you, OK?"

The guest house was located high up in the mountains. Even though it was the height of summer, my room was cold and the bedding **dank**. On top of that the bedcovers were really thin. I froze in the night and had to wear my thick skiing **long johns**. The hinges of the shutters on the window were so rusty that it was impossible to move them even a millimetre. As I lay in bed, the moon shone right into my face. I **screwed up** my eyes and cursed the whole damn adventure. Somewhere in the trees some bird was crooning. Maybe it was a little **tawny owl**.

---

to be bound to – etwas bestimmt tun;
to boost – in die Höhe treiben; to take the mickey – sich lustig machen; to cross one's fingers – sinngemäß: die Daumen drücken; dank – klamm;
long johns – lange Unterhose; to screw up – hier: zusammenkneifen; tawny owl – Käuzchen

It sounded awful, like I was in some **haunted castle** in the mountains. Maybe Carlos and my aunts had been right. I was already lying in bed **trembling**, and the trip hadn't even started. Maybe fear would actually kill me in the end. Rubbish, I told myself. Courage is just a question of training!

I rolled onto my side and thought about the five others who, like me, had been picked out of the flood of applicants and brought to this **godforsaken hole** for one last night in a real bed. Tomorrow we'd be on our way. With food for three days, a detailed **map** of the area, a compass and a GPS unit in our bags, we'd all have to reach a particular **destination** by the evening where we'd find a message telling us the destination for the next day. After doing that for three days we were meant to turn up at some other godforsaken hole by six o'clock in the evening. Every man for himself. We'd each been given a mobile phone for **emergencies**.

Which meant I had two mobile phones in my rucksack. This was because of my two aunts who I'd been living with since both my parents died. After days of "absolutely not! There's no way we're going to let you take part in that **harebrained** competition!" they finally gave me the **go-ahead**.

---

haunted castle – Spukschloss;
to tremble – zittern; godforsaken hole – gottverlassenes Nest;
map – Landkarte; destination – Zielort; emergency – Notfall;
harebrained – hirnrissig; go-ahead – Segen, Erlaubnis

But worse than Aunt Anne and Aunt Lise's reaction was that of my boyfriend Carlos. "What? Without me? The whole time?" he'd cried **irately** in disbelief.

I nodded. "Without you." To be honest, I really **regretted** having to go without him, but after his Wanda-adventure in Morocco – the silly cow had **thrown herself at** him mercilessly, he'd been completely **taken in** by her, and in doing so, he'd **put** our relationship **on the line** – I didn't think it was such a bad idea if he worried about me for a few days. Although by now he should know I'm not a Wanda-type of girl who's only interested in **conquest**, and although I had no plans of revenge in mind, I hoped he'd **be consumed** by jealousy!

To cut a long story short, they made me promise to keep my mobile on at all times. For emergencies, of course, though it was a mystery to me how my two aunts or Carlos in Germany could help me if I got in trouble here.

I jumped out of bed and **peered** out of the window.

The moon was bathing the dense forest in a shimmering silver light. I was in Abruzzi, the

---

irately – empört; to regret – bedauern;
to throw oneself at sb – sich an jmdn. ranschmeißen;
to be taken in by sb – auf jmdn. reinfallen;
to put on the line – aufs Spiel setzen; conquest – Eroberung;
to be consumed – sich verzehren; to peer – spähen

wildest, most **impassable**, remotest part of Italy. There were bears, wolves, foxes, falcons, **golden eagles** and various other unusual animals here, but we were also told there would be a lot of **orchids**. On top of that there might be some **dodgy characters** hiding in the remote corners of the hills from time to time. I'd certainly try to avoid running into them! I put on some thick socks and my fleece-jacket over my long johns and crept back into bed.

Benno, our group leader, greeted us in the morning with a cheerful, "Sleep well, people?!"

We sat down at the breakfast table. The other people in the group were Monika and Mechthild (both eighteen years old), Carsten, Wolfgang, Jonny and me. They were all cool guys with lots of travel experience – except for Jonny. At the official welcome Wolfgang had announced that he and Johannes – known as Jonny – were twins! "We do everything together," Wolfgang had said. "It's really practical: one of us is always bound to be able to do what the other one can't."

"So? What can you do?" Mechthild asked Jonny as he was just **digging out** a thick sketchbook and a box coloured pencils from his rucksack. Jonny

---

impassable – unwegsam; golden eagle – Steinadler;
orchid – Orchidee;
a dodgy character – ein zwielichtiger Typ/Ganove;
to dig out – herauskramen

needed glasses to look into the distance. They dangled around his neck on a colourful cord. But not only that. My eyes almost popped out of my head when Mechthild and I peered over his shoulder: he'd **drawn** us brilliantly in his sketchbook. He could certainly draw, that was for sure.

Mechthild and Monika were really OK. Unfortunately, Carsten was a complete **swot** and a **scrounger**. He had short hair, was athletic, suntanned, **considerate** and helpful, but his antenna seemed to be in a constant state of alert: where's it happening? How can I best get the info? What's important for me?

When breakfast was served, he barricaded himself in with absolutely everything he could get his hands on: the sausages, the cheese, the bread, the tomatoes and cucumber – everything. Pass the butter, please? No way, he **hoarded** everything. But of course, he wasn't going to get away with behaving like that with us.

"It's really great the way you give yourself away, Carsten my boy!" said Wolfgang.

"What do you mean? I didn't say anything," replied Carsten.

"Who said people only give themselves away with words? It's actions which people notice, Carsten!"

---

to draw – zeichnen; swot – Streber; scrounger – Abstauber; considerate – aufmerksam; to hoard – horten

"What did I do?"

"You showed us how **greedy** you are, Carsten! Are you **scared of losing out** or what? Or are you **oblivious** to the fact that other people need to eat?"

Carsten turned bright red and passed the bread and butter.

"There's a good lad, Carsten. **Do unto others as you would have them do unto you**. Try to remember that, OK?" said Wolfgang.

Twins or not, I thought Wolfgang was much nicer than Jonny. Wolfgang had dark blonde hair with **highlights**. He told stories which just made you laugh. I would love to have done the trip together with him. But unfortunately, that wasn't possible.

"Hey, what's with the love letters on the plates?" Mechthild wanted to know.

"Love letters? Those are your hiking routes for today!" cried Benno. "Eat and drink as much as you can. The next few days are **hardly** going to be a picnic!"

I was so excited I could hardly eat anything at all. I made myself an extra **roll**, wrapped it in a paper

---

greedy – gierig; to be scared of losing out – Angst haben, zu kurz zu kommen; oblivious – gleichgültig;
do unto others as you would have them do unto you – was du nicht willst, das man dir tu, das füg auch keinem andern zu;
highlights – helle Spitzen; hardly – wohl kaum;
roll – Brötchen

serviette, and then we were off into the bus. After a short ride up the mountain, Mechthild was **dropped off**. Then we continued. Next was Wolfgang, and after him we drove on a bit more until it was **my turn**.

I stood there on the narrow path, surrounded by nothing but trees, and watched the bus disappear round a corner. I was alone. All on my own somewhere in the middle of Abruzzi. Now all I had to do was hike for three days alone, sleep alone, and in two days' time I had to be in some village called Pescasseroli. Great!

I took the roll I'd brought with me out of my bag, sat down in the middle of the path and listened to the wind in the trees. I felt better after I'd eaten the roll. Then I **spread out** the map, placed the compass alongside it and took out my GPS unit. The letter from breakfast listed the coordinates of my current location as well as those of my evening destination.

It took me a while to get used to everything, taking my **bearings** from the sun and working out where I was going. Then I had a few sips of water and set off.

About two hours later I was on top of the mountain. The view was breathtaking: hills, mountains, valleys, trees, rocks – as far as the eye could see. The

---

to drop off – absetzen;
it's my turn – ich bin an der Reihe;
to spread out – ausbreiten; bearing – Peilung, Position

sun was **beating down** from above as I worked out where to go next, but all of a sudden I froze. Someone was there! Didn't I just hear footsteps? **Twigs** snapping? Stones rattling?

My heart started **pounding**. I held my breath. But after a few seconds I just shook my head. Who knows what I'd heard! There just wasn't a soul to be seen.

I marched on, and the **slope levelled out**. For a while I walked along a flat, grassy ridge. To my left was a deep **ravine**. At its base rushed a stream. Above me buzzards and **kites** swept through the air.

I reached my day's destination at around seven o'clock without any major difficulties or incidents. It was a small **hut**, like the kind a **lumberjack** uses. The key was hanging on a hook right next to the door. I let myself in and, when my eyes had adjusted to the **dim** light, I could make out a narrow iron bed, a table with two chairs in front of the window and an oven with a **saucepan** and a kettle. Lying unmistakably on the table was the second "love letter" of the day.

There's no hurry, I thought, and was relieved to

---

to beat down – hier: herabbrennen; twig – Zweig;
pounding – klopfen, pochen; slope – Hang;
to level out – flacher werden; ravine – Schlucht;
kite – Milan; hut – Hütte; lumberjack – Holzfäller;
dim – dämmrig; saucepan – Bratpfanne

take off my rucksack. I was hungry. Where could I find water? I reached for the saucepan, went out of the hut and spotted a small stream nearby.

The whole thing was starting to be more and more fun. I **crouched** down beside the water and washed my hands and face. **Blimey**, Mimi, I thought, you're a cool girl: brave, fearless and – I jumped to my feet. Someone was there! Someone was definitely there! I definitely heard footsteps! And there – a twig snapped! I listened carefully. I could only hear the wind in the trees and splashing water in the stream. I must be mistaken, I thought, and filled up the saucepan and the kettle. When I went back to the hut, I looked around carefully. No sign of anyone. I was alone.

For the first time in my life I made a fire in an oven. It took a while because at first the **logs** I'd picked out were too big. As I **got the knack of it** and the water in the saucepan slowly began to boil, I spread out my sleeping bag on the **plank bed**, found a packet of candles, which meant I could save the batteries in my torch, lit two of them and, when the water finally boiled, I tipped in the contents of the "vegetable **stew** with noodles" packet.

"I give you my word." I'd promised Carlos and my aunts to call every evening once I'd reached my

---

to crouch – hocken; blimey – Mensch!;
log – Holzscheit; to get the knack of it – den Dreh heraus haben; plank bed – Pritsche; stew – Eintopf

destination. I took my mobile phone out of my rucksack, called up the number and heard Aunt Lise's voice a few moments later.

"Everything OK?" she asked **anxiously**.

"Everything's just great! It was a fantastic day!" I briefly told her about the most important events of the day.

"That's wonderful news! Right, now I'll say goodnight, and remember, Mimi, leave your mobile on at all times. In an emergency there's no time to wait for **reception**, do you hear? You promised us that!"

"Will do!"

Blast! I'd completely forgotten about my promise all day! I put my mobile onto the **window sill**, leaving it on, sat down on a chair, put up my feet on the table and rested my notebook on my lap. "No major incidents," I wrote. "Found the way no problem. Time: 9.44. Now..."

Splash! Crash!

"Bloody hell!" I heard a voice say.

I jumped up and was at the door **in a flash**. As I tore it open, guess who fell into my arms?

"Jonny!"

"Were you expecting somebody else? Blimey! Do we know each other?"

"Come in!"

---

anxiously – gespannt; reception – Empfang;
window sill – Fensterbrett; in a flash – wie der Blitz

"Mimi! Now I recognise you! You're Mimi from our group, aren't you?"

"Of course, I am!"

Jonny looked in a terrible state. His hair was in a mess and was **dangling** into his face, his forehead was smeared with blood, one of the **lenses** was missing from his glasses, his right sleeve had been torn, and I won't say anything about his trousers.

"What on earth happened? And how did you find this hut?"

"Pure **coincidence**. I could just have well not have found it. A bit of luck in a lot of **bad luck**."

"I see. But what happened to you? Shit, the food is boiling over!"

I **leapt** over to the oven. "The precious vegetable stew! Ouch!" I quickly put the pan on the floor and, as I stood upright again, I thought I saw a bright oval shape at the little window. What a load of **rubbish**. I must be seeing things. "Now come on, **spit it out**, Jonny. Why are you here?"

Jonny, the boy with the sketchbook, dropped down exhausted into one of the chairs. He undid the laces of his boot and warily moved his left foot. "It's not **sprained** and not broken, either. I was lucky," he said. "What do you want to know, Mimi?"

---

to dangle – hängen; lens – Brillenglas; coincidence – Zufall; bad luck – Unglück; to leap – springen; rubbish – Quatsch; spit it out – hier: schieß los!; sprained – verstaucht

"What happened to you! And what you're doing in my hut?" I replied impatiently.

"Oh, right. Sure. I'd be **curious** if I were you, too." He grinned and **puckered his** blood-smeared **brow**. "Bad luck got a hold of me and wouldn't let me out of its **clutches**, Mimi!"

"Come on! What are you talking about?" I protested.

"No, really! That's what happened! It was like this: I was the last to get out of the bus this morning, and I tried to find my position and my bearings, but I must have done something fundamentally wrong. I soon came across a ravine and, just as I almost got to the bottom of it, I banged my head and broke my glasses. That was the first piece of bad luck. The second happened when I tried to cross the **stream**."

"You fell in the water, didn't you?"

"Yep. Well, you know, the stones were **wobbly** and slippery. I slipped and tried **to break my fall** with my hands, but unfortunately, I was carrying the GPS unit in my right hand and the compass in my left."

"Oh yeah?"

"Yeah. I lost both of them – the compass and the GPS unit. They both fell into the water and disap-

---

curious – neugierig; to pucker the brow – die Stirn runzeln; clutches – Krallen; stream – Bach; wobbly – wacklig; to break one's fall – den Sturz abfangen

peared before I knew it. The only thing I could save was my life. Or to be exact: my rucksack, me and my life."

"There wasn't much more to save," I said. "And what now?"

"First of all I'm really hungry," replied Jonny **wretchedly**. "Will you share your vegetable stew with me?"

I'd been expecting him to ask that, so I was quick to reply. "Sure, if you share your provisions with me later."

"Sure!" replied Jonny.

I bent down to pick up the saucepan.

"Let me do that," said Jonny, and he picked up the pan and put it on the table. We took our **cutlery** out of our rucksacks and ate hungrily. The saucepan was empty in no time at all.

"So," declared Jonny. "Now we can cook my rations, right?"

The procedure started all over again: boiling water, tipping in the contents of the packet, waiting.

Jonny leant back in his chair and looked around the hut. "We've got it pretty **cosy** here actually," he said. "But I'm wondering where I'm going to lay down my tired little head tonight."

"Ugh?" I looked at him, **dumbfounded**. "The way

---

wretchedly – jämmerlich;
cutlery – Besteck; cosy – gemütlich;
dumbfounded – fassungslos

you talk! I go to bed, turn in, or even **hit the sack**. And you? You lay down your tired little head!"

"Bloody hell, Mimi! You hit the nail right on the head! But seriously, where can I sleep? I suppose you're **laying claim** to the iron bed."

"That's right, Jonny."

"You haven't spotted a spare **mattress**, have you, by any chance?" he asked full of hope.

"Not that I can see. But it makes no difference anyway: you can't stay here. After all, we all promised to spend the days – and the nights – alone! I don't want **to put** my chances of winning the first prize **at risk** just because of you."

"Sure thing," agreed Jonny. "What do you want me to do – roll out my sleeping bag in front of the door? Or maybe I should sleep next to the stream? Then we'd both be alone, but not far from each other, right?"

I **nodded**.

"So what do you say? Can I sleep on the floor here or not? I mean, no one's going to see." He looked at me **in anticipation**.

"OK," I answered hesitantly, "but what are you going to do for the next couple of days, Jonny?"

"You mean I won't be able to find the way, be-

---

to hit the sack – sich in die Falle hauen;
to lay claim – beanspruchen; mattress – Matratze;
to put at risk – gefährden; to nod – nicken;
in anticipation – erwartungsvoll

cause I lost my compass and GPS unit, right? That's true enough. What's more I didn't reach my day's destination, which means I have no idea where I'm meant to go next."

"Don't forget we have to do everything alone..."

"Stop!!" shouted Jonny all of a sudden, **catapulting** me up from my chair. "Another stew is trying to escape! Don't let him go!"

We both rushed over to the oven and **scalded** our fingers on the burning hot **handles**, but together we managed to rescue the precious meal. Jonny took out another muesli stick, announced it was our dessert, and cut it precisely down the middle. Then he resumed the topic. "To be honest, Mimi, I practically disqualified myself today anyway, so there's no point getting worked up about it. Either I hike back or... no, that's not possible."

"Why not?"

Jonny shook his head sadly. "There's no chance of me finding the way with broken glasses. I'm a complete loser in map reading anyway. That's why the only real possibility is the second option."

I put some more wood on the fire and asked, "And what is that?"

"I go with you."

"No way!" I cried **indignantly**. "I'll be disqualified if we turn up together! I already said: I'm not

---

to catapult – schleudern; to scald – verbrühen;
handle – Griff; indignantly – empört

going to **miss out** on my chances of winning just because of you! A week in Sri Lanka!"

"Or Bali, or Cuba," added Jonny. "Sure, I understand. But we could trek the wilderness together until the afternoon of the third day – so that I know **roughly** where the mysterious village of Pescasseroli is – and then we could go our separate ways. You arrive at the **goal** as the glorious winner and I'll **limp** into camp as some stupid loser. So what do you say?"

At first, I didn't say anything. Then, after I'd thought through the situation and failed to find anything dubious, I nodded in agreement. "Why not? We don't know where your destination was for tonight. So we don't know where you're meant to go tomorrow or the day after tomorrow. The only place you could go is back."

"Or with you, Mimi. And that's what I'd like more than anything else. I thought you were…," Jonny coughed slightly, "… really nice from the moment I saw you. Jonny, I said to myself, sometimes people just need the **guts** to make an unusual decision."

"I don't get the connection. What are you talking about, Jonny?" I asked **suspiciously**.

"What's there to explain?"

---

to miss out – verzichten; roughly – ungefähr;
goal – Ziel; to limp – humpeln;
guts – Mut; suspiciously – misstrauisch

"Come on, out with it!" I demanded.

"Mimi! Well… how can I put it… There are… er… there are coincidences and accidents, right?"

"Are you trying to tell me your accident wasn't an accident at all?"

"Of course, my accident was a real accident. But the fact that I didn't head straight back, but went on in the hope of bumping into someone from our group – and of all people I bumped into you – that was a bit of luck in a lot of bad luck, if you know what I mean."

"Right. I suppose you could have ended up finding no one. Or someone else – your twin brother, for instance."

Jonny put his hand on my arm. "Mimi, you're just great. I really like you."

I grinned at him. "Let's see what you say in two days time!"

"Maybe: I love you!?"

"Rubbish! Do you know what? You should wash off that **mud** and blood. There's water outside, but it doesn't run hot from the **tap**!"

While Jonny was washing himself in the stream, I got undressed and **snuggled** up in my sleeping bag.

By now it was really warm in the hut. Jonny came back in wearing his underpants, put the chairs side by side in front of the oven and hung his wet clothes up to dry over the armrests. Then he

---

mud – Schlamm; tap – Wasserhahn; to snuggle – kuscheln

just came and sat down next to me on the bed and said, "I like having a chat before going to sleep. You, too?" He bent down to me.

Just then my mobile phone rang, piercing the night. "Damn!"

I peeled myself out of the warm covers and hopped over to the window.

"Hello?"

"How are you?" I heard Carlos' voice say. "Everything alright?"

"Sure. Couldn't be better," I replied, as was the truth. "How are you?"

"Not so good. I'm worried about you."

"There's no need for that. It's not as if I got lost. I reached my day's destination, ate a packet of vegetable stew and now I'm going to sleep."

Jonny ran the tips of his fingers gently over my arm. I shook my head. He did it again. "Don't do that!" I hissed.

"What did you say?"

"Oh, nothing, Carlos!"

"Hm. What's the weather like?"

"Good," I replied, slightly bewildered. "But since when have you been interested in the weather?"

"I was just asking."

"Carlos..." I said as Jonny twirled his finger through my hair. I **glared at him lividly**. He laughed. "Carlos... I miss you!"

---

to glare at sb lividly – jmdn. wütend anfunkeln

"Yeah? That's good! Are you scared all on your own?"

Jonny **wagged** his finger threateningly and rolled his eyes. I **stifled** a laugh. "Funnily enough no," I replied. "But, you know, Carlos, it would be really nice if you were here," I said. "In fact, I would really like you to be here right now!"

"I'm glad to hear that!" called Carlos. "I'd like to be with you, too. I wish I could be at your side!"

"That'd be great, wouldn't it?" I agreed. "But it's not possible. The distance and all that..." I coughed. "Oh well, it'll all be fine."

Jonny agreed by shaking his head emphatically.

"I hope so! Well then... take care, OK? Think of me. And don't forget: I love you, Mimi."

"Carlos! I don't know you like this!" I cried, **taken aback**. "The loneliness here..."

"...**conceals** a few **perils**," he added.

"It's not as bad as all that," I assured him quickly. "Don't lose any sleep over me, Carlos."

"I hope you're right! Goodnight, sweetie. Dream of me, OK? I'm really close to you."

"Yeah, in mind if not in body!" I shook my head, hung up and put the mobile phone down on the table. "For goodness sake, Jonny!"

"Who was that?" asked my unwelcome visitor.

---

to wag – wackeln; to stifle – unterdrücken;
to be taken aback – alarmiert sein;
to conceal – beinhalten; peril – Gefahr

"My boyfriend, Carlos."

"What? You've got a boyfriend? Why didn't you tell him I'm with you?

I hesitated for a second. "Oh, come on!"

"You could easily have told him that I'd just **got lost** after my fall and ended up in your hut by accident."

"And that because you're so **scatterbrained** we're going to be doing the hike together? What are you thinking of? Carlos would **be at the end of his tether**. He's the jealous type!" I slipped back into my sleeping bag.

Jonny just lay down next to me. Before I could protest, the mobile phone rang again shrilly. "Yes? Oh, it's you again, Carlos. Is something wrong?"

"No, no. Sorry, Mimi, I accidentally pressed the redial button! Bye!"

"Sounds like your boyfriend's just as scatterbrained as I am!" said Jonny **amiably**. "Tell me, Mimi, why do you keep secrets from him?"

"Secrets?" I repeated slowly. "There's only one secret I can think of, and that's the fact that you're with me right now."

"Exactly. Why didn't you tell him that?"

"What? Do you expect me to say: *dear Carlos, can*

---

to get lost – sich verlaufen; scatterbrained – zerstreut;
to be at the end of one's tether –
wie auf glühenden Kohlen sitzen;
amiably – liebenswürdig

you call me back later? I'm just sharing my nightly accommodation with a complete stranger?!"

We laughed.

"So do you have a girlfriend?"

"Sure I do!"

"So? What would she say if she knew I was here?"

"Oh, she'd say something like, 'Jonny, you are a naughty boy! You're a real **waste of space**!'"

"See! She wouldn't like it either if – hey, did you hear that? I heard footsteps! Someone's creeping around the hut!"

"So what? It'll be some hungry fox or a **squirrel**!"

"Jonny! Are you **deaf**? There it is again! And now something's rattling against the window. I'm scared, Jonny!"

"Don't worry. I'm here. Do you want me to take a look?"

He was at the door in a flash and tore it open, but all we could hear were the rustling trees. Apart from that there wasn't a sound.

"It was a **figment of** your **imagination**. Or if it wasn't a figment of your imagination, then it was some **drifter** or other. Or a **serious offender** who had to go underground for a while," explained Jonny. "But don't worry, I'm here."

---

waste of space – Taugenichts; squirrel – Eichhörnchen;
deaf – taub; figment of imagination – Sinnestäuschung;
drifter – Landstreicher; serious offender – Schwerverbrecher

"If you dddon't mind, cccan you ccclose the shutters and sleep next ttto the dddoor, Jjjonny!" My teeth were chattering.

"OK." Jonny closed the shutters and pushed the table in front of the door. Then he spread out his sleeping bag on the floor and sat back down again on my iron bed. It creaked loudly. Normally I would have said, "Hello, Jonny, I don't like it when people **crowd me**. Your sleeping bag's waiting for you," but after the footsteps in front of the door, his being so close to me wasn't such a bad thing. Besides, it was fun hanging out with him.

"Don't you think it's a bit hot?" asked Jonny considerately. "I mean, if I was lying in that sleeping bag, I'd get **heat stroke**. Why don't you undo the zip?"

It *was* hot. I unzipped the bag a little and said, "That's enough."

Jonny chuckled to himself and undid the zip a bit more. "Never do things by half. It's always better to..." The mobile phone rang. "Turn that damn thing off!" cried Jonny.

"I can't. I promised I'd leave it on." I quickly answered the phone. "Yes, Carlos, what is it?"

"Mimi, I'm so worried about you!"

I rolled my eyes. "There's no need, Carlos. Really. I'm fine. I just thought I heard someone creep-

---

to crowd sb – jmdn. bedrängen;
heat stroke – Hitzschlag

ing around the hut, but now everything's quiet. You really don't need to worry about me!"

"But I am! What with you being all on your own. Is everything really OK?"

"Of course, everything's just fine."

Jonny put his fingers playfully in his ears.

"And you won't forget that we love each other, will you?" asked Carlos.

"Yes, you will!" whispered Jonny.

Again I had to stifle my laughter. "Of course not! Especially right now!" I cried.

"That's good, Mimi."

I hung up, shaking my head. "I wonder **what's got into him**," I said to Jonny.

"He's scared of losing you," explained Jonny, **short and snappy**. "I would be, too, if you were my girlfriend."

"He doesn't need to be scared of losing me," I assured Jonny. "If you only knew what I've already been through!"

I told Jonny about my adventures in Canada, Hong Kong and Chile and about how I got lost in the Souk of Marrakech.

"And what about you?" I asked after I finished. "What have you and Wolfgang been through together?"

He yawned. "You know what? I'll tell you about

---

what's got into him – was in ihn gefahren ist;
short and snappy – kurz und bündig

that tomorrow. My watch tells me it's **gone eleven.** Is that possible?"

"Maybe. Goodnight, Jonny."

"What? You're just going to say *goodnight* to me?"

"What else am I supposed to say? *Good morning*?"

"What about a goodnight kiss? A **teeny-weeny** one?"

"You should be so lucky!" I was really angry. "You barge into my hut, demand a place to sleep *and* you want a goodnight kiss? That's going too far!"

"OK. OK," replied Jonny. "**No harm intended**, Mimi."

"I should hope not!"

It took a while for him to get into his sleeping bag. He kept **moaning** and **groaning** about the hard floor, but he wasn't going to get any further with me. "Just be happy you've got a roof over your head, Jonny!"

I was slowly getting tired, and my eyes were almost closing when I thought of a question. "Say, Jonny, why did you apply to take this trip in the first place?"

"There were a lot of practical considerations. My brother, Wolfgang, said: 'Jonny, I know you'll never make it. You'll either get lost in the first hun-

---

gone eleven – elf vorbei; teeny-weeny – winzig klein;
no harm intended – nicht böse gemeint;
to moan – jammern; to groan – stöhnen

dred metres and turn around, or no one will ever find you again. Then the **ravens** will eat you."

"Your brother's obviously got a high opinion of you," I commented sleepily.

Jonny chuckled. "He's talking from experience. His eyes will pop out of his head if I turn up on the third day!"

"I hope he believes your story," I said **apprehensively**.

"And even if he doesn't, he won't **grass on me**."

"I wouldn't be so sure. At the end of the day this is about a whole week in Sri Lanka."

"So what? In the announcement it said 'with a partner of your choice'. We agreed that whoever comes first should automatically choose the other as his partner. All fair and **above board**, right?"

I was **annoyed**. I should have persuaded Carlos or my best friend to take part. Then I would have had double the chances. But now it was too late. I'd have to make it alone.

I woke up very early the next morning. According to my watch it was just before six o'clock. I yawned, rolled onto my side, and wanted to go back to sleep, but something caught my eye. "Jonny! What are you doing!"

---

raven – Rabe; apprehensively – misstrauisch;
to grass on sb – jmdn. verpfeifen; above board – in Ordnung;
annoyed – verärgert

"Look!" He held up his sketchbook to my sleepy eyes.

"That's me!"

"Who were you expecting it to be? Wait a second, just a few finishing touches. So... now you're finished. Do you like it?"

"Do I really look like that?" I sat up and yawned loudly. "My God, you get up early!"

"We've got a lot to do. Light a fire, make some coffee, work out our location and set off. That's a lot."

I looked at him. I couldn't help thinking how different he was from Carlos. Carlos really struggles to get out of bed in the morning, he couldn't draw at all and now, as Jonny sat next to me with his **tousled** hair, he looked really **cute**. I swallowed, quickly thought of Carlos and said, "Then you can already get the fire going."

"I was just about to." He looked anxiously at the small oven. "Where's the switch?"

"What switch?"

"You know, the one to start the fire."

"Are you trying to **pull my leg**? You have to brush out the ash, go and get wood, **stack** it **up** inside, put a match to it and blow. When it's burning you have to add more wood, and then you can put the kettle on."

---

tousled – zerzaust; cute – süß;
to pull one's leg – jmdn. auf den Arm nehmen;
to stack up – aufschichten

“That sounds like a real **hassle**! What do you reckon, Mimi – wouldn’t it be easier to drink the coffee cold?”

“Easier, yes, but do you like cold coffee?”

“No! But under these circumstances I’d be quite happy with it. Anyway, I’m quite sure you’re much better when it comes to **laborious** methods like this one.”

“OK. Then go and get some water.”

“From the stream?”

“Where else?” As soon as Jonny was outside I quickly got dressed and then followed him. He was stalking around the hut like a Red Indian in search of a trail. “Are you looking for yesterday evening?” I teased him.

“No, yesterday’s guest,” he corrected me. “Look, Mimi, someone really was here. Someone who wears Adidas sneakers – I can tell by the footprint. I’ve got the same. That’s **weird**, isn’t it?”

I frowned. “We heard footsteps, do you remember?”

“How exciting!” Jonny stood back up. “But there’s no need to worry. The guy would have attacked us ages ago if he was **up to mischief**.”

I knelt down at the stream, washed my face and hands, and cleaned my teeth. Then I splashed a healthy portion of suntan lotion onto my skin and,

---

hassle – Aufwand; laborious – mühselig; weird – seltsam; to be up to mischief – etwas Böses im Sinn haben

while I was rubbing it in, I spotted the **wrapper** of a piece of chewing gum. It was as fresh as the day – **in mint condition**, so to speak – and the writing was in German. Things were becoming increasingly mysterious. I went into the hut lost in thought and dialled Carlos' number. Didn't he promise I'd be able to contact him around the clock? I waited for a second, and then came the announcement: "The person you are calling is currently unavailable."

I shook my head and dialled my aunts' number at home. "Hello, love, are you OK? Did you sleep well?"

"Everything's just fine, Auntie Anne, but I just found something strange. Someone who was chewing gum must have been sneaking around the hut last night. I found the wrapper."

"Really? That's **careless**... hm, I mean, that's strange. Have you taken a look around the hut?"

"Jon... I was just about to do that!" Blimey, I almost **blew it**!

"Good. Do that. But I don't think there's anything to worry about. If someone **had it in for you**, they wouldn't wait until the morning, would they?"

"That's what I thought!" I cried in relief. "Bye for now then. I'll give you a call this evening, OK?"

---

wrapper – Verpackung; in mint condition – taufrisch; careless – unvorsichtig; to blow sth – etwas verpatzen; to have it in for sb – es auf jmdn. abgesehen haben

We **stirred** our coffee powder into some cold water, ate an apple and some bread and cheese, and after we'd tidied up the hut, we sat down again at the table. I opened the letter. "Hello! By this evening you will have to reach the following destination…" With the compass and the GPS unit we determined the coordinates, checked out the map and set off.

First of all our path took us through a forest, then came a beautiful valley and, just as the sun was at its hottest, we came to a rocky section where there were no trees.

Jonny tied a small towel around his head. "**Sunstroke**'s the last thing I **could do with** now," he said. "How about I tell you something about my life to pass the time?"

"Just a moment." I checked the map, looked at the position of the sun and verified our route. "We have to be careful not to drift too far over to the left."

"Alright. Anyway, you know Wolfgang is older than me..."

"Older?" I asked with a **frown**.

"Yes, he's exactly seven minutes older. But he's not only older, he's smarter than me, too. But then again I can draw a lot better than he can. Together

---

to stir – rühren; sunstroke – Sonnenstich;
can do with sth – etwas gebrauchen können;
frown – Stirnrunzeln

we make the perfect team. We've got pretty cool parents. They've got nothing against us always being on the move – provided we're together and everything's **hunky-dory** in school. We're doing our **A-levels** next year."

I nodded. "Two more years for me."

"In the summer holidays last year we went to the USA for a language course. We wanted to improve our English, but we also planned to stay on for a few days afterwards and go hitch-hiking through one of the national parks. With a rucksack, sleeping bag and tent. It was great, but after two days all that countryside started getting on our nerves, and we got into the next best Greyhound to New York."

"I've never been there," I said.

Jonny laughed. "We hadn't been there until then either. We had no idea that all the youth hostels and cheap hotels in New York are completely booked up in the high season. Even the **grottiest** guest houses were full. It was late at night, and we didn't want to sleep under a bridge with the tramps. We were a long way from a park, and there was no place to go. So we pitched our tent on a **building site**."

"You must be joking!"

"No, it's true. You can't believe how happy we were when we found a few metres which weren't

---

hunky-dory – sinngemäß: paletti;
A-levels – Abitur; grotty – mies; building site – Baustelle

covered by asphalt! You try banging **tent pegs** into **concrete**: it doesn't work – they break in two. Then you can forget your cosy night in the tent!"

"A building site in the middle of New York! I can't believe it! That's so cool!"

Jonny nodded. "Yeah, well. The coolest thing happened the next morning. I woke up because Wolfi was moaning: Brother, **turn down** the radio, I'm sleeping!' I'm telling you, all hell had broken loose outside the tent. There must have been at least a thousand people **convening an assembly** out there. I was just about to shout 'shut up!' when someone opened the front of the tent and poked his head in."

"That was a guy from the building site, I guess."

"Sure, it was a guy from the building site. He looked at us as if we were little green men from Mars. When it finally **dawned** on him that we were from the local planet and not from some distant galaxy, he pointed his finger at us and shouted out to his mates. At first, they didn't believe him. Later on they told us that no one had ever dared to spend the night in the middle of New York in a tent. They also told us that they'd initially thought our tent was a bomb – not aliens from Mars – and were just about to call security!"

---

tent peg – Hering, Zelthaken; concrete – Beton;
to turn down – leiser stellen; to convene an assembly – eine Versammlung abhalten; to dawn – dämmern, klar werden

"Cool!" I was thrilled to bits. "I'd love to travel with you guys."

"The wish is mutual. I've already made the first step," said Jonny with a grin.

"Have you got more stories like that **up your sleeve**?" I asked expectantly.

"Sure. A whole load. By the way, aren't you hungry? I keep looking up at the sun right above us, and it's definitely flashing out a message: 'Hey, people, it's lunchtime! Bon appétit!'"

"My empty stomach says the same," I confessed. We sat down and opened the rucksack. "An apple, bread and some cheese spread. That's all we've got."

"What a perfect meal!" replied Jonny.

We ate our lunch, drank some water and, just as we were about to set off again, my mobile rang in my trouser pocket. I took it out and it stopped ringing, but I could see it was Carlos' number.

"Bad reception," said Jonny with a grin. "I don't understand why Carlos is letting you take this trip. Does he really love you? If you were my girlfriend, I'd have chained you up to the armchair at home. You don't just let a girl who looks like you run off to Abruzzi. There are dodgy guys all over the place."

"And not just guys either," I added. "Carlos was in Morocco recently, and one of the other students, Wanda, tried to **come onto him**. I tell you, the way

---

to have sth up the sleeve – etwas auf Lager haben;
to come onto sb – sich an jmdn. ranmachen

she did it! Just the thought of her **bugs** me even today, Jonny!"

"Oh, right..." For a while Jonny walked next to me without saying a word.

Whenever I thought of Wanda, I saw red. Even now. She'd taken no consideration of that fact that Carlos had told her he had a steady girlfriend. In fact, it seemed to have had the opposite effect, **goading** her **on** even more. And Carlos, the fool, fell for it. By the time he finally opened his eyes, the **thorn** was already deep. Wanda almost split Carlos and me up, no joke. I couldn't help **sighing**.

Jonny and I walked alongside each other lost in thought. The route started to get hillier. The sun beat down on us. There wasn't even the hint of a breeze. And we didn't notice a thing.

We only came to ourselves as we stood right in front of a **precipice**.

"Hey, what the hell is that?" asked Jonny, holding the glasses with one lens in front of his eyes. "How are we supposed to get down that?"

"No idea. The question is: do we have to go down there?"

We sat down and spread out the map. Jonny was the first to realise we'd come a long way off our route.

---

to bug – ärgern, wurmen; to goad on – anspornen;
thorn – Stachel; to sigh – seufzen; precipice – Abgrund

"That's a **real pain**," he grunted. "Several kilometres for nothing."

I took out my compass, compared the coordinates on the GPS unit with the ones on the map and **eventually** said, "If we go down into the ravine and stick to the right, then we can minimise the **detour**."

"OK. We've lost quite a bit of time, but a few minutes extra won't make a difference. Tell me one thing, Mimi…"

I waited. "What do you want to know?" I eventually asked.

He **hummed and hawed** a bit, and then it just seemed to explode right out of him: "Do you love Carlos?"

"Hey!" I cried, taken aback. "That's none of your business!"

"It is to a certain extent."

I stared at him. "What are you trying to say?"

"Oh… nothing. It's all far too complicated."

"Good," I replied impatiently. "Then let's concentrate on trying to get down there."

It was incredibly difficult. First of all, the ravine was at least a hundred metres deep. Secondly, there was no clear path at all. Thirdly, there were **bramble bushes** with extra-long thorns everywhere. Fourthly, where there were no bramble bushes,

---

real pain – echter Mist; eventually – schließlich;
detour – Umweg; to hum and haw – herumdrucksen;
bramble bush – Brombeerstrauch

there were loads of **stinging nettles**. Fifthly, where there were no bramble bushes or stinging nettles, there were nasty-looking rocks.

We got to the bottom covered in **blisters**, half scratched to death by thorns, our hands and knees badly **grazed**, not to mention what our ankles looked like. We threw our rucksacks onto the ground, ripped off our clothes, and in our underpants we jumped into the cold water to soothe our sore arms and legs and pluck out the thorns.

To cut a long story short, we needed torches for **the last leg** to our – my! – night-time accommodation. Jonny was the first to spot the key. He took it off the hook, slipped it into the lock, and was surprised to find the door opened by itself.

We shone our torches into the hut apprehensively.

"Empty. Someone must have forgotten to lock the door," I **concluded**. "Come on, let's go inside. I'm hungry." I pushed past Jonny and went into the hut. "Wow, what a luxury!"

"What? Electricity? A bath with running hot and cold water? An oven and a **freezer** full of provisions? A **dishwasher**? TV?" asked Jonny optimistically.

---

stinging nettle – Brennnessel; blister – Blase;
grazed – aufgeschürft; the last leg – das letzte Stück Weg;
to conclude – schlussfolgern; freezer – Kühlschrank;
dishwasher – Spülmaschine

"Something much better than that! Jonny, you've got your own bed!"

"Oh! Not bad."

"Jonny! You should be happy. It's better than another night on the floor!"

"Who said anything about the floor? But, OK, I've got almost nothing against two beds."

Shaking my head, I dropped my **gear** onto one of them, looked around for some candles, found them and checked out the oven.

"Blimey, Jonny, someone was nice enough to prepare a fire for us! And leave us some matches! And fill up the basket with wood!"

"I don't suppose they cooked for us as well by any chance? A Wiener Schnitzel with **chips** would do me fine. And a large portion of assorted ice-cream with **whipped cream** for dessert. Then cheese, some fruit and an espresso."

"He wasn't quite that thoughtful," I said with a touch of regret.

"What a **goofball**!" grumbled Jonny. "After we had such a tiring day!"

"But the kettle is already full," I spotted.

"It's probably been like that for ages. Are you trying to poison me? Once a mate of mine was in…"

"Point taken," I interrupted him quickly. "Can you get us some fresh water then?"

---

gear – Zeug, Sachen; chips – Pommes;
whipped cream – Schlagsahne; goofball – Doofmann

"OK. And what are you going to do while I do the slave work?"

"I'll kindle the fire and open the powdered soups which we're going to pour into the boiling water. OK?"

"Complicated, cooking, isn't it?" Jonny tossed his ration packet (rice stew today) onto the table and disappeared into the night.

When he returned, the fire was burning **fiercely**.

We looked through our provisions and decided to eat a slice of bread until the stew was ready.

"Theoretically," said Jonny while chewing, "we don't need to be quite so economical with our food. We'll have something proper to eat tomorrow evening."

"We should keep an emergency **supply** – just in case we don't find the village and we need an extra day."

"Or two or three. Or if we never actually turn up," joked Jonny.

We ate the stew, made some tea, and by then I was so tired, I almost fell asleep in my chair.

"Who's going to go out first?" I asked with a **yawn**.

"Go where?" replied Jonny, innocently batting his eyelashes.

---

fiercely – heftig, hier: lichterloh; supply – Vorrat;
yawn – Gähnen

"You know. Out to the stream. Where else?"

"I've already washed."

"Right then, I'll go. Oh dear, I have to call Carlos and my aunts!"

I did that in a jiffy, left the mobile phone on the table, took my long johns out of my rucksack, and went out into the open. It was still very warm, much warmer than the evening before. In the distance there was a **flash of lightning**, but there was still no hint of a breeze. I decided that I'd take the warm long johns off again when I was in my sleeping bag.

As I was washing, I **realised** the stream was deep enough to sit down in. That was just great: I leant back against a rock, felt the water flowing around me, and looked at the flashes of lightning. All of a sudden, I had the feeling I was being watched. I quickly got to my feet, dried myself off and wrapped the towel around me. Of course, no one was there. I was alone, and it would have been a pleasure for me if a nocturnal bird had watched me bathing.

I put on my thermal underwear.

Jonny was already lying in bed. He'd pulled the sleeping bag over his head and seemed to be sleeping. I shuffled over to my bed on the other side of the room with a candle in my hand. Then I blew

---

flash of lightning – Wetterleuchten;
to realise – merken

out the candle and lay down. The iron bedstead heaved a sigh beneath me, and before I could even think the worst – whoosh! – I crashed onto the floor. The whole bedstead had collapsed underneath me.

"Bloody hell! What was that?"

Jonny burst into laughter.

"Was that one of your **pranks**?" I snapped at him, rubbing my bottom.

"I promise it had nothing to do with me! I'm innocent, honest! But I did wonder…," he laughed like a madman, "…hahaha! I did wonder why the foot of the bed was so **crooked**!"

"You could have warned me! Or you could have taken a closer look! And anyway, where are those damn matches?!"

"Have you still got the candles?" asked Jonny.

We **groped** around the floor, but to no avail. Eventually I came up with the **terrific** idea of opening the oven door where I lit one of the candles on the **embers**. Then we finally spotted the matches. But that's not all we saw: two mice **scampered** across the floor.

"Urgh!" I'm not scared of dogs, or wasps, and certainly not of spiders. I'm brave and courageous. But mice send **shivers** down my spine.

I hopped onto a chair, then onto the table, and

---

prank – Streich; crooked – windschief; to grope – tasten; terrific – toll; embers – Glut; to scamper – huschen; shiver – Schauer

stared at the floor as white as a sheet. "I'm going to sleep on the table!" I **whined**. "Or you give me your bed, Jonny! One thing's for sure: I'm not sleeping on the floor!"

"Do you actually think mice could care less about heights? Mimi, they love climbing. Neither a table nor a bed **poses** them a particularly difficult challenge. You'll just have to put up with the fact that we're their guests. After all, they live here all year round!"

"Then catch them, Jonny!"

"OK. Pass me the mousetrap. It's in the wardrobe."

"What are you talking about? There's no wardrobe here!"

"Exactly. And there's no mousetrap either! How am I meant to catch them? Perhaps you could tell me how many of their relatives you want me **to knock off** as well?"

"You **rotten sod**!" I was wide awake. There was no way I'd be able to **sleep a wink** that night. I'd have to wander around the next morning completely bleary-eyed. "Great prospects," I snarled. "I was prepared for everything, but not for sharing my bed with mice!"

---

to whine – jammern; to pose – darstellen;
to knock off – ausschalten, erledigen;
rotten sod – gemeiner Mistkerl;
to sleep a wink – ein Auge zutun

Jonny was laughing his head off. But his laughter dried up quite suddenly as something seemed to **occur** to him, and he shut his mouth to think.

"I know how we can do it, Mimi!" he said. "I can **forgo** a piece of bread, smear it with cheese and leave it on the table as **bait**. The mice will fill their stomachs with the bread and go without you."

"Blimey, Jonny! You're my **knight in shining armour**!" I was really grateful to him. If I hadn't already thought Jonny was a really nice guy, then I would have done so now.

He scratched his head. "Say, Mimi, have you got cheesy-smelling feet? Then we have a problem. The mice are bound to prefer your cheesy-smelling feet to the inferior quality cheese spread."

"I don't have cheesy-smelling feet!" I cried. "I've never had a single cheesy-smelling foot in my whole life!"

"They always come in twos, Mimi," Jonny enlightened me. "But we don't want to **squabble about nothing**. The best thing is we share the bed."

"What do you mean?" I asked suspiciously.

"You on the left, me on the right. Or the other way around. Whatever you prefer."

"Nothing else?"

"Nothing else."

---

to occur – einfallen; to forgo – opfern; bait – Köder;
knight in shining armour – Ritter ohne Furcht und Tadel;
to squabble about nothing – sich über Nichtigkeiten zanken

"Word of honour?"

"Word of honour!" Jonny assured me.

"OK. But first hand me the rucksack, please."

"You're welcome!"

While I put on my thick socks and wrapped the winter scarf around my neck, Jonny prepared a cheese sandwich and put it invitingly in the middle of the table. "Should I leave them a note: 'Dear mice, enjoy your meal!'?"

"In Italian?"

"I thought I'd write it in German."

"Then forget it. Their German is probably not much better than your Italian."

"You're right again. Hey, Mimi, have you got a **sore throat**? Why have you wrapped that scarf around your neck?"

"So that no mouse can creep into my shirt," I replied **sheepishly**. "The scarf is acting as a kind of upper mouse-blockade."

"And the socks? They're acting as a lower mouse-blockade, right?"

"Yes. Can you carry me over, Jonny?"

"Over?"

"Over into bed, Jonny."

"You mean you want me to carry you into my bed?"

"Yes," I said **miserably**.

---

sore throat – Halsschmerzen; sheepishly – kleinlaut; miserably – unglücklich

"I'd be delighted to fulfil your wish, Mimi!"

"You carry me over, and then we say goodnight to each other, OK? Don't get your hopes up, Jonny. My sleeping bag will remain zipped up all night, got it?"

Jonny hesitated. "There's no need to say that, Mimi. I'm not the kind of guy to take advantage of a plague of mice!"

"You're a really great guy," I said, feeling **reassured,** as I put my arm gratefully around his shoulder. "The way you understand me, I could fall in love with you straightaway. But I've got my Carlos."

"Of course. I can't change that, can I?"

"No. Carlos is and will remain my boyfriend."

A few moments later we were lying side by side. I lay there as **stiff as a board**, waiting for the patter of tiny mouse **paws**, but nothing happened. The mice were likewise waiting to hear if the air was clear, but my mobile phone broke the silence.

"Let it ring," said Jonny next to my ear. "I don't like **to mingle with** mice."

We waited for a while, and the phone eventually stopped ringing.

"See?" whispered Jonny. "Your aunts know you're in good hands."

I giggled.

---

reassured – beruhigt; stiff as a board – stocksteif;
paw – Pfote; to mingle with sb – sich zu jmdm. gesellen

The mobile phone rang again.

We waited.

The ringing tone stopped.

I closed my eyes.

The mobile phone rang again. The same thing happened five times **in a row** until eventually I'd had enough. "Watch out, mice, here I come!" I shrieked, leapt out of bed, was at the table in a leap, grabbed the **wretched mischief-maker**, practically flew through the air back to the bed, pressed the green button, and heard Carlos' voice. "Hello, Mimi, how are…"

"Bloody hell, Carlos!" I cried. "Just imagine! There are mice in this hut! Of all things! You know how much I love those little beasts!"

"You poor thing! If I could only do something for you…"

"That's nice of you, Carlos! But I can't talk right now. I have to make sure the mice don't **sneak** into my bed!"

"I'm glad you're only talking about mice," he replied.

"Oh, come on! Bye for now, Carlos!" I said and hung up.

Then the damn thing started ringing again. "This can't be true!" I groaned. "Carlos!!!"

---

in a row – nacheinander;
wretched mischief-maker – verflixter Störenfried;
to sneak – schleichen

"Mimi, don't get me wrong! I'm just really worried about you! Aren't you feeling well?"

"Feeling well? I'm feeling downright rotten!"

"Isn't there something I can do to help?"

"Sure you can help! Send me a few mousetraps!"

"By **air freight!**" whispered Jonny. "Or even better: express courier!"

I put my finger to my lips.

"Mousetraps?" repeated Carlos.

"That's right. You heard me. Mousetraps."

"At least ten of them," whispered Jonny, holding all his fingers in the air. "You'd better order ten mousetraps, Mimi!"

"Hey, Mimi, is someone with you? I just heard a voice!"

"Of course, there's someone with me – the mice, Carlos! That's what's **scaring the living daylights out of me!**"

"Just the mice, Mimi? You're only scared of a harmless little mouse?"

I snorted. "*A* harmless little mouse? What makes you think there's only one of them here? Where there's one, there's a whole **mob** of them! Hundreds! Thousands maybe!"

"Don't exaggerate!"

"You can talk, Carlos!"

---

air freight – Luftpost; to scare the living daylights out of sb – jmdn. zu Tode erschrecken; mob – Menge

"Mimi…"

"Try to understand, Carlos! I can't talk to you right now. I have to keep my eyes on the mice! Goodnight!"

I lay next to Jonny in bed, as quiet as a mouse and as straight as a poker.

"Hey, Mimi, we forgot something," he said a few moments later. "Have you seen the envelope with tomorrow's coordinates in here? I don't think I saw it at all."

I sat up like a shot. "No, Jonny! The envelope wasn't here!"

"Now keep calm, Mimi! I'll get up and take a look around, OK? Maybe we just missed it."

We hadn't missed it. There was no envelope. "Do you think the mice dragged it into their hole?" I asked sheepishly.

"No, I don't think so. No mouse is as heartless as that," replied Jonny earnestly.

"Then Benno must have forgotten me! What a sod!" I hissed. "He doesn't want me to make the running!"

"No, Mimi, that won't be it. But don't you remember – the hut wasn't locked when we got here. It's more likely some drifter came in and took the letter with him."

"So what are we going to do now?"

"We'll just have to use the compass and map to find the way. Do you think you can do it?"

"No idea, but we'll have to try."

It was a very **restless** night. I kept waking up, because the bed was so narrow, and I wanted to make sure the mice weren't advancing. What's more, I was boiling hot in my thermals, thick socks and the even thicker scarf around my neck.

Dawn began to break shortly after four o'clock, and at five o'clock I got up and went outside the hut. The birds were up and about, chirping merrily in the bright morning. But me? The only thing I could chirp merrily about was that the mice hadn't **bothered** me in the night. And then I happened to look at the path – and what did I see? The envelope. A stone had stopped it from flying away. I picked it up and asked myself why Jonny and I hadn't spotted it the previous evening. Of course, it had been dark, but we both went to the stream, and both of us would have spotted a bright, white **rectangle**... Strange.

I shook my head and went back into the hut, where I woke up Jonny. "Hey, look what I found!"

"Where was it?" he asked sleepily.

"In front of the hut. On the path to the stream."

He rubbed his eyes. "That's unreal!"

"But true!"

"I don't get it. Did the mice drop it off there, or what? As a thank you for the tasty cheese sandwich?"

---

restless – unruhig; dawn – Dämmerung;
to bother – belästigen; rectangle – Rechteck

"That's what it looks like."

We grinned at each other. "Come on, Jonny, get up. We have to head off early this morning. I want to win the prize."

We got washed and dressed, and then we stirred our coffee powder into some lukewarm water – this time I'd filled up the kettle the night before and left it on the hotplate. That was before **the antics** with the bed and the mice.

We tidied up the hut again and even managed to get the broken bed back on its feet. We grinned at each other. "Everything hunky-dory!"

After deciding which direction to take, we set off.

It was a beautiful day, warm, but not hot, with a few fluffy clouds in the sky and a gentle wind. We made good progress. At around midday we saw a few houses in the distance. "Do you think that's our village?" I asked.

"It's a bit too soon, don't you think, Mimi?"

"Let's take a look."

No, we soon found out that the houses didn't belong to "our" village, but it wasn't far from here now.

"Jonny, I think we'd better go our separate ways now."

"Take it easy, Mimi! Listen, that thing I wanted to say to you yesterday, well, it's just..."

---

the antics – das Theater, der Zirkus

"Spit it out!"

"It's not that easy, Mimi," said Jonny **bashfully**, rubbing his nose. "I told you yesterday that I have a girlfriend."

"Yes, that's what you said," I confirmed.

"Well, it's not true. It was a lie. I don't have a girl-friend. Not a hint of one. Honest."

"So why did you say it then?"

"I was just **boasting**. I'm sorry."

"OK. I've forgotten it already."

"Good. Thanks. But..."

"Yes?"

"I'd like one."

"Sure! Who likes being single?" I replied. "No one's stopping you from looking for a girlfriend, are they?"

"No, of course not. It's just: I don't want to look for a girlfriend."

"Man, you're getting on my nerves!" I cried. "What do you want?"

"The subject of the question isn't right," replied Jonny quickly. "It should be *who* do you want?"

"Alright then. *Who* do you want?"

"You, Mimi."

"What on earth am I supposed to say to that?

"Simple. Try 'I want you, too, Jonny'!"

"Man, you're terrible! You know I've got a

---

bashfully – verschämt; to boast – angeben

boyfriend! And anyway, why bring up the subject now, when we're in such a hurry?"

"I needed time to think about it," replied Jonny sheepishly. "I can't think that quickly, Mimi."

"You can't think quickly," I sighed, "but you expect me to? Give me time, Jonny. I'll write you an e-mail, OK?"

"When?"

"In a week's time."

"I can't wait that long."

"I need a week," I insisted.

"Alright. One week. On one **condition**: that you stay here for five more minutes, Mimi."

"Five minutes?!"

"Please, Mimi!"

He dropped his rucksack to the ground and put his arms around me. "Your nose is sunburnt," he whispered. Then we kissed.

It ended up being more than five minutes. When you've saved someone's life, like I have, and shared **humble** forest huts with that same person for two long nights, and when he returns the favour by **decoying** mice with his precious cheese sandwiches, then it's **inevitable** that feelings develop.

We kissed and kissed. I forgot all about Sri Lanka and Carlos – until a **fir cone** landed beside us. It

---

condition – Bedingung; humble – bescheiden;
to decoy – ablenken, locken; inevitable – unvermeidlich;
fir cone – Tannenzapfen

seemed to have come out of nowhere. It literally fell out of the sky and broke the spell.

"I have to get on," I said. "Do you know the way, Jonny? Are you sure you'll make it?"

"Of course. See you later."

I ran and ran, and after half an hour I saw the first houses and **rooftops** of Pescasseroli. Our meeting point was the *Albergo di Cesare* and Benno had said that the hostel was at the village centre. I looked for the main street and had just turned around a corner, when I saw Wolfgang, Jonny's twin brother. He was looking at his map as an old man **came shuffling up**, and Wolfgang asked him the way. That was my chance to speed past him and run along the street. Wolfgang started running after me, but to cut a long story short, I reached our destination one and a half **yards** ahead of him, and in doing so I won the first prize: a week in Sri Lanka with a partner of my choice!

The others also arrived safe and sound before six o'clock. Only Jonny turned up later, just as dusk was falling. He was in such a pitiful state with his filthy shirt, torn trousers and broken glasses that everybody felt sorry for him and believed his story. I just gave him a wink. "Wow! You made it with

---

rooftop – Dachgiebel;
to come shuffling up – angeschlurft kommen;
yards – hier: Schritte

nothing more than a map in your hand and the sun over your head? Not bad!"

"I am," said Jonny humbly, "just **one hell of a great guy**!" He opened his sketchbook on the table. "Look! Do you recognise this village?"

"Pescasseroli!" cried Monika, grabbing the book. "Did you draw anything else? Show us your other pictures!"

I almost had a heart attack: our secret! My first prize was in great danger!

"Nnno," stuttered Jonny, looking at me and turning red. "They're of no interest to you."

I nodded in relief. "You can't share private memories with just anyone, right?"

We sat next to each other for the rest of the evening and at breakfast the following morning. Unfortunately, we didn't have any time alone together to talk. People from the group kept turning up and disturbing us. Only when we said goodbye to each other did Jonny briefly **give me a hug**, whispering into my ear, "Have you thought about it yet?"

I hesitated. "Yes. As you know, I've got a boyfriend."

Jonny looked so disappointed I almost gave him a kiss to comfort him.

---

one hell of a great guy – toller Teufelskerl;
to give sb a hug – jmdn. umarmen

The following afternoon I was back at Rome airport, waiting for my flight to Stuttgart. I was just drinking a coke, when I almost **fainted**.

"Carlos?" I asked tentatively. "Is it you or am I seeing ghosts?"

"It's me."

"What… what are you doing here?" I stuttered. "Why aren't you at home in Germany?"

At first Carlos looked at me a bit **irritably**. Then he put his arms around me and, like Jonny the day before, he said, "Your nose is sunburnt."

"Come on, **spill the beans**. What are you doing here in Rome?"

"I was looking after you, Mimi."

"What's that supposed to mean?"

"Simple. Your aunts and I didn't want to spoil your fun, but we didn't want you to go through the wilderness on your own. So I got all the necessary information from Benno and…"

"He wouldn't have given it to you!"

"Oh yes, he did. Because you were the youngest participant, and because I gave him my word not to make any contact with you, he gave me the information. I followed you everywhere, all the time, and during the night I pitched a one-man tent near your hut. It wasn't such a big deal… No, following you wasn't such a big deal at all."

---

to faint – in Ohnmacht fallen; irritably – vergrätzt;
to spill the beans – „auspacken", erzählen

I didn't have **the foggiest idea** what he was talking about. "But?"

"But when that Jonny guy turned up and he tried to **chat** you **up**... that, Mimi... that was **hell.** I saw everything, and I had to keep my mouth shut the whole time!"

"Keep your mouth shut? You? You kept calling me!"

"So what? I had to **keep him in line** somehow."

My heart missed a beat. "The footsteps in front of the door... the chewing gum wrapper... the envelope on the way to the stream... the wood in the oven..."

Carlos put his finger to his **chest**. "That was me!"

I slowly began to **grasp** what the poor guy had been through. I broke into a smile, and then I laughed and laughed until the tears **trickled** down my cheeks. Carlos shook me. "Stop it, Mimi! You don't laugh about love! I mean it seriously!"

"Really?"

"Yes! When I think of Jonny..."

"And when I think of Wanda," I added softly.

Carlos **gulped**. "Are you going to see Jonny again?"

---

the foggiest idea – die leiseste Ahnung;
to chat up – anmachen; hell – Hölle;
to keep sb in line – jmdn. in Schranken halten;
chest – Brust; to grasp – begreifen; to trickle – rinnen;
to gulp – schlucken

"What about Wanda?"

We looked at each other for a long time. Then we kissed. After that we both knew that neither Wanda nor Jonny would ever play a role in our lives again.

Carlos was the partner of my choice. I'd fly with him to Sri Lanka. Who else?!

Bianka Minte-König

Summer Downpour & Holiday Amour

"Forget it!"

Franzi looked at me **in astonishment**. "But, Kiki! I thought you'd be the first to say yes!" She looked really disappointed.

"What made you come up with *that* idea?" That's what I'd really like to know. Me and an **adventure cycle tour**? You must be joking! My **backside** was an open wound after a short ride to school! And now Franzi had got it into her head that it would be really funky to ride all the way to the North Sea! No, sir, not with me. And anyway, the North Sea smells like **pee**!

I wanted to go to Mallorca! To Alcudia, to Playa Jardin, to see that cute **rep** from last year. The way he **chucked** my brother into the swimming pool – that was a scream! Especially since my brother, the little joker, couldn't even swim at the time, and we had to **make a joint effort** to save him. But when

---

in astonishment – erstaunt; adventure cycle tour – Erlebnis-Radtour; backside – Hinterteil; pee – Pipi;
rep – hier: Animateur; to chuck – schmeißen;
to make a joint effort – etwas mit vereinten Kräften tun

we both jumped into the water our heads collided, leaving me seeing nothing but stars rather than my drowning brother. André, the rep of bad luck, obviously had a harder head than me, but I must have caught him at a very sensitive spot, because he sank to the bottom like a stone. This was something I realised as the stars slowly started to fade away. It left me facing the urgent question: who do I save first?

I decided to follow **tried and tested wisdom** and, according to the sayings *sisters do it for themselves* and *every man for himself,* I first decided to swim to the edge of the pool so I could **assess** the situation properly. And then – if required – get help of course! I mean, I couldn't just let my brother and the mega-cute rep **drown**!

But as I pulled myself out of the pool, **a miracle occurred**: a small, wet hand grabbed mine – a little **Sea God** was standing next to me, huffing and puffing in his soaking wet Eminem **bandana**, water trickling over his face. My brother, the joker, had been saved!

I grinned at him, deeply relieved.

And before I could ask how this miraculous rescue had occurred, he blubbered at me, "I can swim!

---

tried and tested wisdom – alterprobte Weisheit;
to assess – einschätzen; to drown – ertrinken;
a miracle occurred – ein Wunder geschah;
Sea God – Wassermann; bandana – Kopftuch

You won't believe it! I can swim! Underwater too. I came up all by myself and swam over here! Real swimming, with arms and legs, like you taught me..."

Superb! And good to know. But where was André? I **was just about** to take a look around when something grabbed my leg underwater.

I shrieked, "Urgh, a **shark**, a shark! It's going to eat me..." and as it pulled me underwater, my last words gurgled into the waves washing over my head.

I tried to make out my attacker underwater. Of course! The dead live longer! It was none other than André pulling another **practical joke**. The guy just couldn't get enough!

I hammered my fist against his broad chest. He grabbed my hand, pulled me towards him and gave me a wet underwater kiss on the lips before we both shot upwards. We reached the surface, panting for breath and laughing.

"You could have killed him!" I gasped.

"Who?"

"My brother! He couldn't swim until just now."

André laughed his deep, bear-like laugh. "And you couldn't kiss underwater until just now, right? But you can learn everything with André! I'm the best rep on the island!"

---

to be just about – gerade im Begriff sein; shark – Hai; practical joke – Schabernack

"**Poseur**!" I slammed my hand onto the surface of the water and sprayed him in the face.

"Wait there, you **cheeky mermaid**!" he shouted as I quickly swam off.

Franzi's **offended** tone of voice tore me out of my daydream, straight out of last year's summer holiday, back to the reality of planning this year's summer holiday. "I don't understand why you don't want to come. Greetje is joining us, and Lea, too. Even Mona's said yes. If we ask Meik and Bastian, they'll probably join us as well..."

Meik and Bastian. Now Franzi was **bringing up the big guns**. Meik on a cycle tour with Mona while I was away in Mallorca – no way, I wouldn't be able to **sleep a wink**!

"Rubbish! Meik will never ever come with you. He's bound to be going to France with his mum or dad." I remembered that he'd mentioned some holiday home over there and had **raved** about it.

"Maybe he doesn't want to go there this year."

"And why not?"

"Because he'd rather go on the cycle tour with you, **for instance**."

---

poseur – Angeber; cheeky mermaid – freche Wassernixe; offended – beleidigt; to bring up the big guns – schweres Geschütz auffahren; to sleep a wink – ein Auge zutun; to rave – schwärmen; for instance – zum Beispiel

Very **flattering**, but it was hard to believe. Nor did I want to believe it. As much as I liked being with Meik, holidays were holidays, and I preferred to spend them under the Spanish sun rather than a **drizzling** grey sky at home. But I had to admit it: there would be a strong risk factor if Meik did go with them. Even if her boyfriend Bastian came along as well, Mona would always remain a sex bomb with a constantly ticking **time fuse**. And the moment when she exploded might come sooner than any of us ever **expected**.

"OK! I'll sort it out with Meik," I said after having pictured Meik and Mona on the tour. And at the back of my mind, I was still hoping Meik would come with me to Mallorca...

But there was no way he would.

"No, Kiki," he **refused** without **hesitating** when I brought up the matter. "Mallorca's out of the question. I haven't got enough money. Mum wants to renovate the flat, so our budget's looking **pretty tight**."

That was a blow in the face!

"But a bicycle tour isn't for free either!"

"No, but it's much cheaper than a trip **abroad**,

---

flattering – schmeichelhaft; to drizzle – nieseln;
time fuse – Zeitzünder; to expect – erwarten;
to refuse – ablehnen; to hesitate – zögern;
pretty tight – ziemlich knapp; abroad – ins Ausland

with flight and all. I was planning to go on a canoe tour with the club, but when Franzi told me you really wanted me to go with you, I gave myself a **kick**." Meik looked at me affectionately with his blue eyes. "You know I can never **turn you down**."

I must be suffering from acute hearing loss. I couldn't believe what I just heard! How could Franzi have the nerve to talk Meik into this when I hadn't even agreed to go on the bike tour in the first place. Nor would I ever agree! EVER! Certainly not now. I'm not going to let people **blackmail** me.

"Come with me to Mallorca!" I tried again. "It's much better there. I'll ask Dad if he can lend you the money. I'm sure he will. You can pay him back in stages." I smiled. That was really a mega-cool idea.

Meik looked at me **glumly**. Then he shook his head. "I know you mean well, but I'm not going **to get myself in debt** just for a quick holiday. And certainly not with your dad."

Hm, on the one hand I could understand that, but on the other hand I couldn't think of anything more **divine** than whispering sweet nothings into Meik's ear under the southern sun.

---

kick – Tritt, hier sinngemäß: Ruck;
to turn sb down – jmdn. enttäuschen, hängen lassen;
to blackmail – erpressen; glumly – niedergeschlagen;
to get oneself in debt – Schulden machen;
divine – himmlisch, göttlich

But he was as **stubborn as a mule**.

Pah! I could be stubborn as well. Just try me! "And there's no way I'm going to spend my summer holidays rubbing **blisters** into my **bum** on some **overland pedalo**. I want to go swimming, lie about on the beach, and read cheeky books. I have absolutely no ambition to break the record for last-man-in-the-cycle race with a **runny** nose under constantly pouring German rain."

I was quite **convinced** that – as far as fitness was concerned – I would always **bring up the rear**. That's right, not everybody can be a sporting genius!

"Kiki?"

Oh no! When Meik puts that **velvet** touch to his voice, then negotiations are out of the question. I wasn't going to let him twist me around his little finger and **sweet talk** me into anything.

"Kiki, it'll be great! The whole gang, it'll be fantastic... camping, youth hostels, barbecues and singing... Having fun... and swimming in the North Sea, sand and – I bet you – there'll be **loads of** sun!"

I looked up at the grey sky. "Loads of sun? I can't

---

to be as stubborn as a mule – stur wie ein Esel sein;
blisters – Blasen; bum – Po;
overland pedalo – sinngemäß: Drahtesel;
runny – hier: triefend; convinced – überzeugt;
to bring up the rear – das Schlusslicht sein;
velvet – Samt, samten; sweet talk – säuseln;
loads of – jede Menge

see any at all. Who do you take me for? Yvonne Catterfeld? But I can't move the clouds for you!"

"Wouldn't be such a bad thing," he said with a really cheeky grin. "Kiki, you're just too pessimistic. A rainy June doesn't mean the weather will be bad in August!"

"Oh no? Doesn't it? Are you aware of the date today? Yes, exactly. **The Seven Sleepers.** And what does that mean? Well, you **clever clogs**?"

Meik looked at me with a strange expression on his face – like he thought I was a bit mad.

"The Seven Sleepers! **Got it**? No? Then I'll tell you. When it rains on the Seven Sleepers, it means it'll rain for the next seven weeks. Got it? And do you know what that means? Exactly! It's going to rain right through our holidays! At least here in Germany!"

Meik shook his head in disbelief. "But that's just a **superstition**."

"No, it's not! It's an **old farmers' saying**. And old farmers' sayings are written in my grandmother's hundred year-old calendar which is never wrong."

"Kiki, you're **off your rocker**!"

"Do you wanna bet?"

Meik waved his hand dismissively, but then he seemed to have second thoughts. "OK. Let's bet.

The Seven Sleepers – Siebenschläfer; clever clogs – Schlaumeier; got it? – kapiert?; superstition – Aberglaube; old farmers' saying – Bauernregel; to be off the rocker – spinnen

But you'll have to check the outcome of the bet yourself. I bet there won't be a drop of rain on our bike trip. Are you going to take it on?"

"Pah! Sure I'll take on the bet. You'll all drown. The cycle paths will be transformed into bottomless **bogs** which will swallow you up! The way things look today, it will rain at least as much as it did the last time we had summer **floods**. But, go ahead, if you really want to bet."

Meik grinned **mischievously**. "OK. Deal. The bet's on, and you're coming with us to check it out!"

He'd **caught me hook, line and sinker**, the trickster! "Never! I'm going to fly my backside over to Spain's sunny beaches by airbus, not torture it on some rock-hard bicycle saddle. And neither your sweet talking nor your **crafty** bets can stop me. And that's the end of that!"

When I got home, I started having second thoughts too. What was I doing? I wasn't usually as super cool and **uptight** as that. My period must have been coming up. That sometimes made me really **unbearable**. The old hormones! What a **pain**! Basically the idea of a cycle tour was really great, and

---

bog – Sumpf; flood – Hochwasser;
mischievously – heimtückisch;
to be caught hook, line and sinker – voll erwischt;
crafty – hinterhältig; uptight – zickig;
unbearable – unerträglich; pain – hier: Mist

now I was annoyed with myself for blowing my chances of going with them. There was no way I could go back now. I still had my pride. It was a shame I'd missed the bike, as they say!

The tables turned not because of my late realisation, or Meik's trick, or Franzi's **skills of persuasion**, but all because my aunt Sophia gave birth to her fourth child very **prematurely**, and Mum wanted to rush off to southern Germany with my joker brother to look after our various underage cousins while Auntie Sophia took care of little Linda in the clinic's **incubator**. "It's the least I can do for my sister in this situation." Mum threw herself wholeheartedly into her Mother Teresa role and **disregarded** my arguments.

"But I need a Mallorca holiday!" I whined, full of self-pity. "I can't live without sun! I get depression. I **wilt** like a flower in the absence of light."

"Don't talk nonsense. We Central Europeans get by perfectly well with our weather conditions without having to wilt. Or do you think I look wilted?"

Well, **don't shoot the messenger**, but I thought I'd better keep my mouth shut.

---

skills of persuasion – Überredungskünste;
prematurely – verfrüht; incubator – Brutkasten:
to disregard – nicht beachten; to wilt – welken;
don't shoot the messenger – mach den Boten nicht für die Nachricht verantwortlich

"I thought you wanted to do a bike trip with your class this year? Franzi's mother asked me what I thought of the idea recently at parents' evening."

Oh no! Not that as well. Why did our mothers have to **poke their noses in**?

"I thought it was a great idea, though we'd have to make sure that an adult accompanied the group somehow or other..."

Huh? An adult accompanying us? Well, great. If I had indeed, in my moments of weakness, toyed with the idea of going with them, my mother's confession restored my **resilience** at once. Besides, I was old enough to know what was good for me, and that was anything but a silly bike trip through silly, wet, northern Germany.

"Then I'll just stay at home on my own and sit in front of the **box**," I sighed with some resignation.

The idea seemed to **bother** Mum. "You certainly won't be doing that, my dear," she said with a touch too much kindness. "If you don't want to go away with your friends – which is something I just don't understand – then you can come and help me look after Auntie Sophia's children."

"No way! That's pure blackmail! **Forced labour**!

---

to poke the nose in – die Nase reinstecken, sich einmischen;
resilience – Widerstand; box – Glotze;
to bother – hier: nicht gefallen;
forced labour – Zwangsarbeit

That's... that's illegal under the **Protection of Young Persons Act**! Even children have the right to holiday!"

It was really nice of her to be there for her sister, and normally I might have gone and helped her out, but I'd really **slogged my guts out** in school that year and just had to have a break. My nerves wouldn't be able to **handle** a mass of screaming little kids. No, I couldn't do that to Mum – me running around her like a bundle of nerves while she was under stress. I was doing that enough at the moment.

I had an idea. "I can go and stay with Dad in Berlin."

My dad was a Member of Parliament, and he had a small apartment near Alex. There was always a lot going on around there in the summer. Gay festivals, pop concerts, a lot of fun and action.

I was **over the moon** with my idea. That's just what I'd do. Cycle tour? Forget it!

But Mum threw a **spanner in the works** again. "Your father is with a delegation in China, you know that perfectly well. You don't actually think I'd let you hang out in Berlin on your own, do you?"

Protection of Young Persons Act – Jugendschutzgesetz;
to slog one's guts out – schwer schuften;
to handle sth – mit etwas umgehen können;
to be over the moon – ganz begeistert sein;
to throw a spanner in the works – einen Strich durch die Rechnung machen

"No?"

"No, certainly not! And there's nothing you can do about it."

Things went – as was always the case with us – **to and fro** for a while. I got all worked up, and Mum's patience eventually ran out.

"Now that's enough!" she exclaimed, **exasperated**. "Bike trip or southern Germany! Think about it. There's no other choice."

I rushed out of the kitchen to my room and **slammed the door shut** behind me. Mum should know I'm angry, even if a part of me could understand why she didn't want me staying at home on my own or hanging out in Berlin. But it was still **nasty** of her to put me under such pressure.

I threw myself onto my bed, grabbed my mobile and called Franzi. "It's all your mum's fault," I **barked** into the phone.

"Huh? Why's it her fault?"

"She talked my mum into making me go on the bike trip with you!"

"Really? That surprises me." Franzi was clearly **playing it innocent**. "I've no idea how she came up with that."

"Oh no?"

---

to and fro – hin und her; exasperated – entnervt;
to slam the door shut – die Tür zuknallen;
nasty – fies; to bark – bellen;
playing it innocent – unschuldig tun

"What did your mum think about the idea?"

"Stupid question! Why don't you ask me what *I* think about the idea?"

"OK. What do you think?"

"I don't have a chance to think anything! I'm being blackmailed."

Did I just hear a **stifled giggle** on the other end of the line? "And what form does this blackmail take?"

"Babysitting, **mollycoddling** screaming children, washing pots and pans, peeling potatoes – **in a nutshell**: forced labour for my aunt's little monsters – or a bike trip with you."

Now it was unmistakable. Franzi could hardly hold back her laughter any longer. "And so you decided to go for the little monsters?" she said, bursting out into laughter.

I held the phone away from my ear, and when she'd calmed down, I **hissed**, "Exactly. And I hope you have a nice time!" Then I hung up. That'll give her something to **chew** on!

A few seconds later my mobile started buzzing and vibrating at the same time.

Of course, it was Franzi, utterly **beside herself**.

---

stifled giggle – unterdrücktes Kichern;
mollycoddling – pampern, beruhigen;
in a nutshell – kurz und gut; to hiss – fauchen;
to chew – kauen, knabbern;
to be beside oneself – außer sich sein

"You don't mean that seriously, do you? You can't possibly prefer idiots like that to us!"

"Can't I?"

"No!"

Now it was my turn to laugh. "Don't worry, I don't! Do you think I'm a **suicide case**, or what? I'd rather go with you!"

This time I hung up the phone on an overjoyed Franzi. "Great! I have to tell Greetje and Lea straightaway! That means the *Pepper Dollies* are all together!"

The *Pepper Dollies* – that was our girls' club, and if all of us went on the trip together, it was **bound to** be a party.

Franzi wasn't the only one who had calls to make. I also had to tell someone the happy news. How would Meik respond to my change of tune? Would he still be angry?

"Meik?"

"Yeah, Kiki? What's up?"

"I've got some news. I think I will check out the bet myself and... come with you."

Hearing Meik so over the moon sent a **tingle of excitement** down my spine. As I hung up and put the phone down next to my bed, I couldn't help smiling to myself at the thought of the trip. If, at that moment, I'd had even the faintest idea of what

---

suicide case – Selbstmordkandidat;
to be bound to – bestimmt sein, werden;
tingle of excitement – prickelnde Vorfreude

I was letting myself in for, then I would have gone on my knees to my mother and begged her to please, please take me with her to my aunt's **stinky-bummed-midgets**!

The first day began with the loveliest drizzle. At the same time Mallorca was going through a serious **heat wave**. Great! I might well win the bet with Meik **hands down**, but for what? A pair of wet feet!

We met at the station because we planned to do **the first leg** to the **moor** by train. We'd already checked in our bikes the day before. They'd be waiting for us when we reached the destination of our first leg. Mum drove me to the meeting point with my rucksack and sleeping bag in not exactly the best of moods. All at some unearthly hour of the morning, of course.

Maybe I really should have gone for the alternative of **spoiled brats** in southern Germany?

When I got to the station, I was **knocked for six**. Franzi had dragged along the world and his wife on this cycle tour. It had a fatal similarity to a school trip. It wasn't just Mona who got on my nerves straight away, standing there arm in arm with Bas-

---

stinky-bummed-midgets – Stinke-Po-Zwerge;
heat wave – Hitzewelle; hands down – haushoch;
the first leg – die erste Etappe; moor – Heide;
spoiled brats – verzogene Gören;
to be knocked for six – vom Schlag getroffen werden

tian while **engrossed** in a conversation with Meik, but the rest of the male population, too. For crying out loud, did Franzi have to bring Raffi along? And I didn't really have any opinion on Lea's latest **conquest**, Torsten. Now all we needed was for Greetje to drag along some guy.

And that's just what she did! **My chin hit the ground** as I saw her father, our art teacher – alias van Gogh – turn up. And if my eyes didn't deceive me, he was pushing along a **Dutch** lady's bicycle as well.

It soon became clear that he'd been given the task of being our adult **supervisor**. I think I'm going to **faint**! was the first thing that came into my head. He was the last person I'd have thought of for a sporty trip like this.

"Well, you know..." he said somewhat **bashfully** after saying hello, "... Greetje begged me to come along so the whole trip wouldn't be cancelled. She literally got down on her knees, so here I am. Is that alright with you?"

"Sure," Franzi and I cried in unison. Van Gogh was OK really. He was one of the few teachers who hadn't completely forgotten he'd been young once as well.

---

engrossed – vertieft; conquest – Eroberung;
my chin hit the ground – mir blieb der Mund offen stehen;
Dutch – holländisch; supervisor – Aufsichtsperson;
to faint – in Ohnmacht fallen; bashfully – verschämt

I looked at Mona out of the corner of my eye and wondered what she was chatting to Meik about. He was literally hanging on her every word and hadn't even noticed that I'd arrived. If this is just the beginning, I might as well have stayed at home! Look, just to make it perfectly clear: I've got nothing against Mona. Honest. It's just that she's – how can I put it? – got the kind of personality that makes a girl **get edgy** when she's around boys, **let alone** your own boyfriend. From the moment she turned up in my class – with her long hair, her perfect figure and her **easy-going attitude** – she had a snake-like hypnotic effect on the boys. They **flocked** around her like **vultures,** helplessly caught under her **spell**. And the most absurd thing was there was nothing she could do about it. She went through life as the picture of innocence, a quality which just drove me **up the wall**. Inside. But I didn't let it show on the outside. Besides, she was always very friendly and funny.

But, nonetheless, my blood was beginning to boil as I saw the way Meik was clinging to her. Fortunately, before I was stricken by **jaundice**, Meik finally deigned to notice me.

---

to get edgy – nervös werden; let alone – geschweige denn;
easy-going attitude – lockere Art; to flock – sich scharen;
vulture – Geier; spell – Bann;
up the wall – sinngemäß: auf die Palme;
jaundice – Gelbsucht

"Kiki!" he called over to me – with what was, in my opinion, a rather **exaggerated** sense of **delight** and took a few giant strides towards me, where he took my rucksack off my back. "Give that to me. Wow, that's heavy! What have you packed? Wacke-stones?"

"That's a perfectly normal rucksack, not the big, bad wolf!" Does he think I'm some old **nanny-goat** who fills up wolves' stomachs with stones or something? He was **laying it on a bit thick**! I wasn't really into compliments like that. Things could get hot around here!

I glanced over to Mona. Why had her boyfriend put his arm around her when mine was just telling me Grimm's fairytales?

The train came roaring into the station just then, thank God, and the next thing on the agenda was to divide ourselves up between the various **compartments**. Needless to say, Meik immediately dumped his **gear** next to Bastian, and I had Mona on my heels whether I wanted her or not. I dropped down into my seat with a sigh and stared at her. One thing was for sure: if this trip wasn't going to turn into a complete nightmare for me, I'd have to change my attitude to her. Perhaps I might

---

exaggerated – übertrieben; delight – Entzücken;
nanny-goat – Mutter Geiß;
to lay it on a bit thick – ziemlich dick auftragen;
compartment – Abteil; gear – Zeug, Sachen

be able to learn something from her. I really liked the way she was so easy-going with Bastian... I couldn't help grinning as I came up with a great idea. I'd copy Mona! Exactly! Like a clone. I'd do everything she did with Bastian directly with Meik. It would be a real turn up if I didn't have the same charm or effect on my boyfriend as she did on hers. When Meik sat down next to me, I immediately tried it out: I grabbed his arm and put it around my shoulder. Nice and cuddly!

But instead of putting his arm around me **properly**, like Bastian did with Mona, he pulled it back and said, "Do you want a **roll** as well? I'm really hungry. I didn't even eat any breakfast."

Well then! Bon appétit.

While he was eating, I looked out of the compartment window – at the rain.

We'd already been **on the move** for some time when the **ticket collector** came around. There was trouble straight off. Van Gogh had decided to play our watchdog pretty late in the day. Although he had a ticket for himself and one for his bike, he hadn't reserved a place in the **transport carriage** for his bike.

---

properly – richtig, anständig; roll – Brötchen;
on the move – unterwegs;
ticket collector – Schaffner;
transport carriage – Güterwaggon

"It's not such a **big deal**," he said to the female ticket collector. "It's perfectly alright in the **aisle**."

"You're not in a position to **judge** that," disagreed the woman **tersely**. "The aisle is not a storage space. Your bike is blocking people's passage."

Van Gogh started to get a bit **irritable**. "What would you suggest I do?"

"Get out at the next station and make a reservation. The storage spaces for bicycles are all occupied in this train. And without a reservation you have no right to have your bike transported."

We couldn't believe it, but there was nothing to be done. At the next station the ticket collector waved over one of the railway attendants and, before van Gogh knew it or we could do anything about it, his bike had been **dumped** onto the **platform**.

"What am I supposed to do now?" cried van Gogh in utter **dismay**. As a Dutchman, the whole thing must have been completely incomprehensible to him. It was just another example of German bureaucracy.

"You'd better get out," advised Bastian. "Otherwise you might never see your bike again."

That seemed like the best solution to all of us, so

---

big deal – hier: großes Problem; aisle – Gang;
to judge – beurteilen; tersely – kurz angebunden;
irritable – ärgerlich; to dump – abstellen; platform – Gleis;
dismay – Entsetzen, Bestürzung

we handed van Gogh his rucksack, which had all his papers inside, and left him behind with his bike. We wouldn't be seeing him again soon.
We'd only just picked up our bikes at our destination when van Gogh called us on the mobile. The next bicycle storage space on a north-bound train was **available** in two days time. That was too long. If we waited for him, we'd miss the **ferry** to the island of Wangerooge. And it was almost as impossible to get tickets for another ferry at this time of season as it was to transport a bicycle by train.

We cursed German Rail.

"What are we going to do now?" whimpered Greetje. "Without adult supervision?"

Bastian and Meik chuckled.

"Well, if you ask me," said Meik, "we should start the cycle tour on our own. After all, Bastian and I both have **youth leader certificates**. Van Gogh can try to catch us up."

No sooner said than done. Bastian got on the phone and **settled things** with Greetje's dad. Our adult supervisor took a note of all our daily destinations and promised to catch up with us as soon as possible.

Whichever way he could. It was a good thing he could always reach us by mobile.

---

available – verfügbar; ferry – Fähre;
youth leader certificates – Jugendleiterschein;
to settle things – die Situation klären

Although it's hard to believe after all the **to-ing and fro-ing**, at some point later we did actually find ourselves heading northwards on some narrow cycle path alongside a country road. Northwards towards the land where the sheep watch over the **dykes** and baa when they flood – or something like that. Or was it geese that **cackle** when danger is nigh? Whatever. It was probably all three: sheep, geese and – if it continued to rain like this – floods as well.

We'd put on our raincoats, wrapped our rucksacks and **panniers** in plastic, and fearlessly set off on our tour, **scoffing** at the threat of catching a cold. Our destination: the beautiful island of Wangerooge, which, according to Franzi and Meik's calculations, would take three days to reach. I just wanted to see if I'd survive the first!

Meik, Franzi and Bastian were **exuding expertise** as they explained the route stooped over a bicycle map.

It led us through a tourist area which was well worth seeing. Yes, well... it would have been worth seeing if we could have made it out behind the wall of rain.

As we headed into one of the typical local villages straddling the road and went around a sharp

---

the to-ing and fro-ing – das Hin und Her;
dyke – Deich; cackle – schnattern;
pannier – Satteltasche; to scoff – verachten;
to exude expertise – Sachverstand verströmen

bend, a huge **workhorse** suddenly galloped out of a field towards me. I slammed on the **brakes** and **skidded** past the huge creature's tail with **screeching** tyres. The horse brayed and – as if it had just been called – a tiny **steed** shot out of the same meadow and immediately clung to the hooves of the workhorse.

"A pony! What a sweet pony!" cried the **horse-loving halfwit** Lea without delay. "Shall we try and catch it?"

"Sure," I replied dryly – as far as you can be dry in the pouring rain. "Ask Meik where he packed the lasso."

Mona, who had in the meantime hurried over, laughed at my joke, while Lea just looked at me somewhat **bemused**.

We cycled on while the two stray horses trotted along in front of us down the main street of the village. We didn't **dare** try to overtake them, and we just stayed at a safe distance. I kept thinking that a car might shoot out from behind the next corner any minute and **sweep** the two horses off the road.

Mona seemed to be thinking something similar and said, "One of us has to do something!" and she pedalled at high speed to catch up with the horses.

---

workhorse – Ackergaul; brake – Bremse; to skid – schlittern;
screeching – quietschend; steed – Ross;
horse-loving halfwit – Pferdenarr;
bemused – verständnislos; to dare – wagen; sweep – fegen

I copied her, though I rode alongside the pony while she was next to the workhorse. She called something out several times, and eventually the workhorse stopped in its tracks. What on earth was the magic word?

"Brrrrrrrrrrrr!" I bawled into the pony's ear from behind.

It shook its head brusquely, kicked its legs and ran sideways into the driveway of a detached house.

Someone opened a **hatch** in a door. "Hey, get your pony off my property!" shouted a kids-kitchen-no-career woman at me.

"That's not *my* pony!" I **growled** back at her.

"So why are you scaring the poor animal like that?"

"The poor animal scared *me,* not **the other way around.**"

"Horses are very sensitive. You don't shout into their ear!" she **nagged** at full volume.

"I'm very sensitive, too, when people do that to me!" I hissed back at her.

In the meantime the others had gathered around me, and Mona did the most disgraceful thing. She came sauntering around the corner with the run-away workhorse in tow, leading it by its **bridle** like a **placid lap-dog.**

---

hatch – Luke; to growl – knurren;
the other way around – andersherum; to nag – keifen;
bridle – Zügel; placid lap-dog – sanftes Schoßhündchen

A flash of recognition lit up in the face of the **country bumpkin**.

"That's farmer Jürgens' young Else. So that must be Fidelius." She turned around and shouted into the house, "Svantje, Fidelius is trampling around the garden. Get him out of here and ride him over to farmer Jürgens." And then she turned back to us and – in a slight more friendly tone – inquired if there was, "Anything else?"

Mona and I looked at each other.

"No," said Mona. "Just this once we won't charge you anything for catching them, but if Else and Fidelius keep doing this, the **horse butcher** will probably get called in soon. They can't always get lucky with oncoming traffic!"

"Horse butcher!" An eight-year-old country bumpkin with fair hair and freckles snapped at us. "There aren't any horse butchers around here! We ride horses, we don't eat them!"

"Nor do we," said Mona **timidly**. "I was just trying to say it's dangerous for them if they get hit by a car..."

"Cars don't do that around here. They know horses **roam freely**."

Oh, well, in that case... I grabbed my bike and got back on. I preferred it to riding a live monster like these two horses.

---

country bumpkin – Landei; horse butcher – Pferdemetzger; timidly – ängstlich; to roam freely – frei herumlaufen

Mona looked uncertainly between us and the workhorse. "And what shall I do with him now?"

"Give him a **slap** on the bum and send him home."

Mona slapped him on his behind, and Else placidly started to stroll off, following the pony.

"For crying out loud," I groaned as I imagined what would have happened if I hadn't braked quickly enough and had **hammered** into the workhorse from the side.

"Forget about it," said Franzi before the full horror of the scenario had unfolded in my mind. "There won't be horse goulash today!"

"But now you mention it," remarked Raffi, "eating wouldn't be a bad idea."

So we decided to ride on for a bit until we found an **affordable** place to eat, which we did.

We peeled off our rain clothes, steaming hot and cold, and threw them onto the **rustic benches** of the pub. There was a hearty stew with sausage on the menu and, after the **landlord** had reassured us that the sausages definitely weren't the product of horses involved in road accidents, we **tucked in**.

After eating we got back on our bikes, and soon my bum started aching, just as I had expected. I couldn't help thinking about a nice **cushion** tied to

---

slap – Klaps; to hammer – brettern; affordable – preiswert;
rustic benches – rustikale Bänke; landlord – Wirt;
to tuck in – reinhauen; cushion – Sofakissen

my backside. That wouldn't be a bad thing. Bicycle saddles were far too hard for my **delicate physique**! Unfortunately the fine drizzle didn't wane, and at dusk a mist rose from the fields and mingled with it to form a white, impenetrable wall.

"Lets look for a **bed and breakfast**," insisted Lea, who'd also had enough by now.

But Meik said we only had a few more kilometres to go until we came to a farmer who let people stay in his **barn**. He'd found this piece of worldly wisdom in an alternative travel guide for nature lovers and **eco**-freaks. "We can get fresh milk there and make ourselves **cosy**."

That's what I said. Probably some eco-farmer.

It was already dark when we got to the farmhouse which was situated somewhat **off the beaten track**. The barn was empty, and the farmer was rather **baffled** that we didn't want his cosy guestrooms, but wanted to sleep in the cold barn instead. I mean, if someone had asked for my opinion... But no one did.

So we took up quarters like the finest soldiers of the German army. We hung out our soaked clothes over the farm machinery to dry and clambered up

---

delicate physique – zarter Körperbau;
bed and breakfast – Pension; barn – Scheune;
eco- – Öko-; cosy – gemütlich;
off the beaten track – abseits gelegen;
baffled – verdutzt

a **wobbly** ladder into the barn's upper gallery which was filled with hay. After a major **hay fight** we laid out our sleeping bags for the night.

I was utterly exhausted by the time I slipped into my sleeping bag and happened to glance over at Mona who was lying lengthways in Bastian's arms. Grrr. **Envy** crept up in me.

Why was Meik so complicated? Couldn't he just sit next to me and give me a loving hug as well? No, he had to spread out the map and plan the route for the following day. I was in even more of a bad mood as I watched Franzi **cuddling up** with Raffi and Lea **having a snog** with her Torsten.

"It's absolutely freezing," I said in the hope of getting a cuddle.

"You're right," said Meik. "It is pretty cold for this time of year. There's usually twelve hours of sunshine around here in August and an average temperature of twenty-eight degrees."

"Oh, really?"

What a botched job! I didn't want to hear the weather **forecast**, I wanted him to move a bit closer, take me in his arms and give me some body warmth. Not a chance!

"OK, people!" Meik eventually called out as he packed away his map. "Let's go to sleep!" After

---

wobbly – wackelig; hay fight – Heuschlacht; envy – Neid;
to cuddle up – kuscheln; to have a snog – knutschen;
what a botched job – so ein Mist; forecast – Vorhersage

glancing at Mona and Bastian, he added with a word of warning, "Everybody in their own sleeping bag. Don't forget we promised van Gogh we wouldn't let him down."

Bastian and Mona giggled. "But we're not."

Franzi came over to me with Raffi.

"Really! The way Mona throws herself at Bastian!" said Franzi **disapprovingly**. "It's totally **inappropriate**. I'm glad Meik warned them. I wouldn't put it past her if she sneaked into Bastian's sleeping bag with him!"

I couldn't help thinking, "What would be wrong with that?" And, without thinking about it, that's just what I said to Franzi.

"Well, I prefer to sleep in my own sleeping bag," said Franzi. "You, too, I guess?" She looked at me for solidarity.

She'd made it quite clear that sharing sleeping bags wasn't her thing, and to be honest not mine either. So I was quite pleased about Meik's **announcement**.

He made a point of looking at his watch. "It's ten thirty. If we really want to **set off** early in the morning..."

Then he gave me a goodnight kiss and slipped off

---

disapprovingly – missbilligend;
inappropriate – unangebracht;
announcement – Ansage;
to set off – aufbrechen

like a good boy, an example to the others, into his one-person sleeping bag.

Raffi also hit the sack.

We *Pepper Dollies* had settled down in the hay in the corner, and Mona now came over to join us. So much for sneaking off into Bastian's sleeping bag! She wasn't as stupid as Franzi thought.

I was freezing cold. What a **crap** summer!

After we'd finished bedding down, I glanced over to Mona's sleeping bag. There was no sign of movement. On the other side of the room Bastian sounded like he was sawing up half a forest with his snoring. Then I cuddled up into my sleeping bag and fell asleep, my **mind at rest**.

The second day began as the first had ended. *And the rain, it rained every day…*

Meik had taken pity on us because of the **awful** weather and agreed to let us have breakfast in the farmhouse. This **revived my spirits** so much that, contrary to all expectations, I actually managed to saddle my bike afterwards. Even though my bum was screaming, "Don't do it! Don't do it!"

I **clenched my teeth** and pedalled as if I wanted to win the Tour de France. And I almost did. I kept

---

crap – beschissen; the mind at rest – beruhigt;
awful – grauenhaft;
to revive the spirits – die Lebensgeister wecken;
to clench the teeth – die Zähne zusammenbeißen

imagining I was Jan Ullrich making a final sprint for the **yellow jersey**, but the shiny yellow object in front of me was only Meik's anorak, and it was simply impossible to **catch up** with the guy.

In the end I dropped back and waited for Franzi to catch up with me. "But I'll get him in the **time trial**," I gasped.

"Time trial?" Franzi looked across at me, puzzled. She obviously wasn't **clued-up** when it came to professional cycling. But who cares!

Bastian **whizzed** past us, and Mona pulled up alongside.

She seemed to have had a good night's sleep and was in a cheerful mood. "Turn on the sun!" she said to me.

"Sure, no problem. Where's the switch?"

She laughed. "Maybe we should do a sun dance."

"Sun dance?" Franzi was surprised. "I only know rain dances."

"Oh no!" I exclaimed. "We've got enough rain as it is!"

After a few hours I was so soaking wet I could have wrung myself out.

"Let's take a break!" called Raffi, and we were **unanimously** in support of this idea.

We found a picnic spot in the woods – which

---

the yellow jersey – das gelbe Trikot; to catch up – einholen; time trial – Zeitfahren; to be clued-up – auf dem Laufenden sein; to whizz – zischen; unanimously – einstimmig

even had a roof over it – so we could at least butter our rolls in the dry. The scenery was really quite beautiful, and if the weather had been a bit better, we could have enjoyed it a lot more. If the weather had been a bit better!

In the meantime news had arrived on Greetje's mobile from our adult supervisor: van Gogh (and his bike) had managed to catch a train home early that morning. He'd have to change trains several times, and it would take him at least five hours to get home, where he planned to jump into his car and join us at our next overnight stay. Well, great!

Mona sat squeezed up next to Bastian, and the two of them fed each other pieces of bread and sausage. Sweet. I must try that with Meik! I slipped up close to him, broke off a piece of my roll and was just about to slip it into his mouth with a tasty piece of liver sausage when he said ironically, "Look at the two of them. They're like a pair of **monkeys**. Any moment now Mona will start chewing his food for him."

My hand with the piece of roll froze in mid-air on the way to Meik's face. Then I quickly pulled it back before I made a fool of myself. I stuffed the piece of roll into my mouth and couldn't help being **annoyed** by the fact that Meik was much less romantic than Bastian.

As we rode on, my **mood** was as cool as the air temperature. I sighed. What was wrong with me?

---

monkey – Affe; annoyed – verärgert; mood – Laune

Even when I did the same as Mona, I kept **putting my foot in it**, whereas everything she touched seemed to turn to gold.

But at least I wasn't the only unlucky one in our team. My ingenious boyfriend Meik had led us onto a particularly charming cycle path which only had one **hitch**: it stopped in the middle of nowhere.

When Meik suggested turning around and cycling back to take another path, I thought I was going to have a **nervous breakdown**.

"How many kilometres is that then?" Franzi asked as she hopped uncomfortably from one foot to the other. Her bum was obviously sore as well.

Meik hummed and hawed. "Yeah, well… to be honest, there's only one other path and… to get there we'd have to… let's just say… well, I'd say…"

"How many?!" Even Bastian was **holding a gun to** Meik's **head**.

"Ten to fifteen kilometres."

"No! That can't be true!" shrieked Franzi.

"And what if we go over the fields to the next road? We don't always have to take a **picturesque** cycle path," suggested Lea. "You can't see anything of the scenery in the rain anyway."

---

to put the foot in it – ins Fettnäpfchen treten;
hitch – Haken;
nervous breakdown – Nervenzusammenbruch;
to hold a gun to sb's head – jmdm. die Pistole auf die Brust setzen; picturesque – malerisch

"Exactly. The quickest way is the best way," I agreed with her.

So we'd all soon agreed – although Meik advised us against it strenuously – and we continued **cross-country**. The first bit, on a **timber path** through the woods, was bumpy but just about rideable. But then it came to an end, and we had to push our bikes through the **undergrowth**.

Livingstone, I thought, steaming rainforest, the **luggage-bearers** sinking into the **bog** – pure adventure! We had it all, just with bikes instead of luggage-bearers, and it was us who were sinking deeper and deeper into the sodden forest floor.

"An **edible** mushroom! Look, a really huge edible mushroom!" exclaimed Mona all of a sudden, absolutely thrilled.

For crying out loud, how can anybody notice something like that in this situation? I wouldn't have even noticed if an anaconda had **dangled** down from one of the branches and licked my face.

"Leave it," said Bastian to Mona as she was about to pluck it out of the ground. "We can't cook it."

"That's a shame! Then I'll take a photo." Mona took her camera out of bag and – click! – the mushroom was **in the can**.

---

cross-country – querfeldein; timber path – Holzweg; undergrowth – Unterholz; luggage-bearer – Lastenträger; bog – Sumpf; edible – essbar; to dangle – baumeln; in the can – im Kasten

Eventually we came to a forest fence.

"Let's look for the gate," suggested Meik. "Most of the time fields have farms nearby, and that means there are roads, too."

I'd be utterly delighted, I thought, as I looked at my mud-encrusted sneakers. My feet were already soaking wet, and it wouldn't have made any difference to me if this jungle excursion continued with a march through some **soggy** grassland. For a change I was Atréju on his way to the ancient Morla. The main thing was this trip wouldn't turn into a never-ending story!

But my imagination was soon **drained**. Pushing loaded bicycles over fields was so **strenuous** that I was soon sweating, not just all over my body, but in my brain as well. I couldn't even think. I just **staggered** half dead behind the others, taking it step by step. *There is no way back… da-dam!*

We had to pass through a **flock** of sheep, but what would normally have provoked cries of delight, was now a smelly nightmare. Damn, they smelt like a lorry full of wet pullovers without **fabric softener**. Hardly as fresh as April!

Then came the cows. Black and white ones. Big. Huge. Wild and dangerous!

---

soggy – durchnässt; drained – erschöpft;
strenuous – anstrengend;
to stagger – torkeln; flock – Herde;
fabric softener – Weichspüler

"For goodness sake, woman! They're cows, not Spanish bulls," said Meik as Lea **refused** to go past the animals.

"And how do you know?"

"Look at them! Can't you see what's hanging between their legs? Do they look like bulls to you?"

I looked as well. No, those **udders** full of milk didn't remind me of bulls at all. They were clearly cows. **Dairy cows**!

Greetje threw down her bicycle. "I'll milk one of them," she said. "A sip of warm milk right now would be just the right thing."

"You're off your rocker!"

"Why? Come on, bring your plastic cups over. I once milked a fake cow at an agricultural show in Holland."

"But this one's real," I hastened to point out.

And it had four legs to walk away on. Which is what it promptly did when Greetje **grabbed** its udders. The cow gave itself a shake, **wobbling** its udders to and fro, and the milk spurted right into Bastian's face instead of into the cup he was holding out. Then the cow escaped to one side, brushed Franzi across the face with its tail and knocked Raffi over with its large backside. He fell back with a cry and landed bum-first in a warm **cowpat**.

---

to refuse – sich weigern; udder – Euter;
dairy cows – Milchkühe; to grab – packen;
to wobble – schwenken; cowpat – Kuhfladen

"I want to go home!" wailed Franzi as she took in the smelly catastrophe.

I could have had all of this in southern Germany, I thought. But in a somewhat more hygienic setting of **disposable nappies**!

The cleaning process took some time, though Franzi eventually managed to talk Raffi into doing a striptease. There was no way he could continue sitting on the saddle with his **soiled** trousers.

Thus the day's journey went on, but at some point – though only just – we arrived half dead and utterly exhausted at the farm where we could bed down for the night.

"I'm not cycling any further!" Franzi had decided to go on strike the next morning.

Maybe I should do the same?

But Meik and Bastian took out the maps and showed us that it really wasn't all that far to the ferry to Wangerooge. Even if it was still raining, the last leg looked pretty **easy-going**.

"Where's van Gogh got to?" I dared to ask. Not that I couldn't get by without adult supervision, but he'd said he was going to join us here.

"The **bicycle rack** on his car was broken. He had to order a **spare part**, and it only arrived this morn-

---

disposable nappies – Wegwerfwindeln; soiled – besudelt; easy-going – leicht zu schaffen; bicycle rack – Fahrradträger; spare part – Ersatzteil

ing. He said he'd meet us at the ferry." Meik grinned as he told us this change of plan.

I also had to smile to myself. If it went on like this, the trip would be over before our supervisor had even got there.

"Our ferry leaves at four o'clock. We shouldn't have any problem making it. And if we leave straight away, it'll be easy," explained Meik, hurrying us along.

OK, OK! Take it easy! If only reality always **reflected** the theory, but, of course, it never did. This time it was down to me. No, I didn't fall into a cowpat – at least I was spared that – but I did get a **flat tyre** about ten kilometres from the ferry port. That was about an hour and a half before the ferry set sail.

"Right then, on the double!" said Meik, quite the happy **handyman**, as he dismantled my panniers with Bastian and turned the bike upside down. "Where's your spare **inner tube**?"

"Er, inner tube? Me?"

"Don't tell me you took a trip like this without any spare parts?"

"Hum, yes, well, to be perfectly honest… I don't usually take trips like this… so I normally don't need anything…"

Meik resigned himself to this piece of informa-

---

to reflect – hier: entsprechen; flat tyre – platter Reifen; handyman – Heimwerker; inner tube – Schlauch

tion and went over to his pannier. "Alright, I'll use my gear then." When he saw the miserable expression on my face, however, he smiled. "At least it'll stay in the family!"

It was so sweet the way he said it. I forgave him for his arrogant tone immediately and made out that only men could repair bicycles. I mean, if it was such an inner need for him, then I didn't have to get my hands dirty myself. I wasn't half as **ambitious** as him.

But I soon gathered that things weren't really working out by the way Meik and Bastian kept **cursing**.

Franzi started to get nervous and kept looking at her watch. "Come on, boys," she **pestered** them. "We have to get a move on. Otherwise the ferry will leave without us."

After what seemed like an eternity the experts were finished, and we could get back on our bikes. What followed was a race against time.

We'll never make it! I kept thinking as I pedalled like a madman. This time I would have won any time trial, but would that be enough for us to catch the ferry?

I didn't feel the rain anymore. Besides, sweat was streaming down my bright red face and the gallons of water in and outside my clothes were mixing to-

---

ambitious – ehrgeizig; to curse – fluchen;
to pester – drängeln

gether. My breath was hot and spasmodic. I was just thinking that I was going to fall off my bike any second when I saw the white buildings of the **harbour**!

Our ferry sounded its **fog-horn**.

Oh no, it was going to **set sail** in front of our very eyes! That would just be so **cruel**!

We sprinted over to the dock and would have rushed straight onto the ferry had a sailor not been standing on the gangway. He asked us for our tickets and told us that – needless to say – our bikes had to be taken on board at a different place. They were as stubborn as German Rail.

We must have all looked so completely **shattered** that – thank you God – the guy didn't make any trouble.

After briefly looking at his watch, he called over two colleagues who'd taken our bikes on board before we even knew it. We got on board just as quickly and dropped into the seats in the passenger hall. Dry at last!

I shot up from my seat a few seconds later when Greetje **shrieked**. She jumped up and threw her arms around her dad's neck. He'd made it to the ferry only a few minutes after us. Well then, everything was just hunky-dory!

---

harbour – Hafen; fog-horn – Nebelhorn;
to set sail – Segel setzen bzw. ablegen; cruel – grausam;
shattered – fix und fertig; to shriek – aufkreischen

The youth hostel on Wangerooge was in a tower and was really great. We girls had a big cosy bedroom just for us and the first thing we did was go to bed. And we **slept like logs**!

The following day it was misty, but – what a miracle! – it was dry.

"Come on, Kiki, I'll show you the beach."

I went past the **groynes** hand in hand with Meik until we came to a really pretty beach of sand dunes. It was low tide, and the receding water was leaving behind all sorts of **flotsam and jetsam** to which the seagulls were swooping down with shrill cries in search of something edible.

"Oh, look!" exclaimed Meik all of a sudden. He bent over and picked something up. When he turned around to me, he was beaming all over his face. "Open your hands."

I hesitated, because I thought he might be **taking the mickey** and was going to drop something **gross and slimy** into my hands.

Meik grew impatient. He grabbed my hand, opened my fist and put something cold inside.

What was it? A stone? It was far too light for that. Curious, I opened the palm of my hand and stared

---

to sleep like a log – wie ein Stein schlafen;
groyne – Wellenbrecher;
flotsam and jetsam – Strandgut;
to take the mickey – einen Scherz machen;
gross and slimy – eklig und glitschig

inside. Wow, that was fantastic! A huge, honey-coloured lump of **amber**.

"It's a present," said Meik. "That's the sun we've been missing until now!"

As Meik kissed me, the clouds above us broke and a shower of rain teemed down.

And that's how it remained for the rest of the holiday – for many a long, wet kiss.

Although Mona, who caught a nasty cold, and the others in the group continued to despair at the bad weather, I'd managed to find the **pot of gold** at the end of the rainbow. I had my own sun – my amber sun – and, believe me, it warmed my heart, that's for sure! We made a hole in it, and I wore it around my neck on a leather string. I'd won the bad-weather bet but, despite the rain, I'd had the best holiday a girl could wish for.

Dad took pity on me. "What a rainy holiday," he said to **console** me. "Listen, I've got a few air miles left. How about three days in Mallorca?"

What a question. Hello, sun, here I come!

A few hours later I was lying by the pool.

It was just like last year. Same hotel, same swimming pool, same rep.

André welcomed me with an "hola, guapa!" Then he threw one of the many bikini-beauties

---

amber – Bernstein; pot of gold – sinngemäß: Goldschatz; to console – trösten

into the water, presumably to give them a lesson in underwater kissing. He **fooled around** just like back then, a big friendly bear with a sense of fun, who chanted into the mini-disco **mike**, "If you're happy on vacation, clap your hands…"

He hopped around on the open-air stage, and I watched him from my deckchair. Last year I'd **given it my all and done** the club dance myself.

The sun shone.

I sighed, leafed through my cheeky girls' book and thought about Meik, the **rainswept** cycle tour, and the many wet kisses. The amber stone was hanging around my neck.

What on earth was I doing here? "Dad," I asked. "When are we flying home?"

---

to fool around – herumblödeln; mike – hier: Mikrofon;
to give it one's all and done – begeistert mitmachen;
rainswept – verregnet

Hortense Ullrich

Wednesday 9th July

"I don't think you **scared him away**, Jojo." Lucilla shook her head. "Not on your life! Not Sven! God knows, he's been through enough with you anyway!"

"What's that **supposed to** mean?" I asked huffily.

Lucilla looked at me with wide open eyes. "Oh, come on, be honest! Who else would put up with the chaos you always cause without **complaining**?"

As Lucilla and I continued to walk along, I thought about what she'd said. She was right. The fact that Sven hadn't called me for two days and seemed to have been swallowed up by an **earthquake** probably had no **significance** whatsoever. We'd been together for ages, and Sven had the pa-

---

to scare sb away – jmdn. vergraulen;
to be supposed to – sollen;
to complain – sich beklagen; earthquake – Erdbeben;
significance – Bedeutung

tience of a **saint** with me. That was **down to** his sense of humour. And my mum always said I was only **bearable** if you either had a sense of humour or some pretty strong **sedatives**.

I was so lucky to have Lucilla!

I gave her a big smile. "You're right, Lucilla. I really don't have any reason to panic!"

But Lucilla seemed to have second thoughts. "On the other hand..." she said, thinking out loud.

I was **racked with doubt**. I stopped in my tracks and grabbed Lucilla's arm. "What?"

"What do you mean, 'what'?"

"You know, what do you mean by 'on the other hand'?"

"Oh, right, yeah..." Lucilla took a deep breath. "Now don't **get** all **worked up**, but..."

"I never get worked up!" I snapped at her.

"...if you think about all the **expectations** you've had of Sven until now," continued Lucilla doggedly, "you might be able to understand him if he did..."

My voice almost broke as I **persisted**. "If he did what?"

---

saint – Heiliger; sth is down to – etwas liegt an;
bearable – erträglich;
sedatives – Beruhigungsmittel;
to be racked with doubt – von Zweifeln geplagt werden;
to get worked up – sich aufregen;
expectations – hier: Zumutungen;
to persist – beharren

Lucilla shrugged her shoulders apologetically. "You know, if he..."

"**Dumped me**?" I cried, almost beside myself. "Is that what you're trying to say?"

Lucilla **recoiled, taken aback**. "Oh no, of course not. I meant if he... if he... needed a break!" She smiled, relieved.

"A break?"

Lucilla nodded. "Yes, like a Jojo-free period."

"A Jojo-free period?" I mumbled **flatly**. "That's the beginning of the end! And at the start of the holidays of all times! Great!"

Lucilla put her arm around me to comfort me. "It's OK, don't blame yourself."

We walked on towards the ice-cream parlour in silence. After a while she asked me, "What did you say to him when you saw each other for the last time?"

I **flinched**. "The *last* time? My God, Lucilla, how can you say a thing like that!"

"What did I say? I just wanted to know what happened when you two... er ... well, the last time you... Oh, dear, Jojo, I can't think of another word! What did you talk about?"

I **sniffled** and shrugged my shoulders. "I don't know."

---

to dump sb – mit jmdm. Schluss machen;
to recoil taken aback – erschrocken zurückfahren;
flatly – tonlos; to flinch – zusammenzucken;
to sniffle – schniefen

"Come on, make an effort. Think! Maybe you said something that..."

"...scared him off?" I cried dramatically, breaking down into tears.

Lucilla gave me a **nudge**. "No, something that could help us out... something that could explain why he..."

I looked at her despairingly. "Go on, say it: something that could explain why he doesn't want to have anything to do with me anymore!"

Lucilla waved her hand dismissively. "Rubbish, stop thinking so negatively! Maybe he's just had an accident."

"You're not just saying that to make me feel better?"

"Not at all!" said Lucilla. "It might be."

I smiled again and **gave** Lucilla a grateful **hug**. "You're right. That's so nice of you. That's **bound to be** the reason why he hasn't called!"

I continued walking along, now fully **at ease**. Yes, that was it: Sven wouldn't leave me; he'd probably only had an accident.

I suddenly stopped in my tracks. "An accident? Oh my God, Lucilla!"

Lucilla turned to me with a look of alarm.

---

nudge – Knuff;
to give sb a hug – jmdn. umarmen;
bound to be – bestimmt sein/werden;
at ease – beruhigt

"An accident!" I shrieked hysterically. "What kind of an accident?"

"How should I know? It was just an idea!"

"A really stupid idea!"

"Then tell me what you talked about when you met for the last... two days ago."

"Are you going to take the accident theory back?"

"Yes."

"Good," I sighed. "It was great fun, as always. We were at the swimming pool, and Sven caught me a **fried sausage**."

"He did what?"

"It was a joke. He had a stick and some string with him, and a fried sausage was dangling on the end of it. He said it was really fresh, because he'd just fished it out of the pool."

Lucilla looked at me with wide open eyes.

"You know what he's like! I almost died of laughter... So that can't have been the problem."

"Wasn't there anything else?" Lucilla enquired persistently.

"No... apart from the thing with the mayonnaise."

"What thing with the mayonnaise?"

I sighed. Did I really have to tell the story? It was a bit **embarrassing**.

---

fried sausage – Bratwurst;
embarrassing – peinlich

I took a deep breath. "My mum had been shopping, and I'd asked her to buy me some suntan lotion. When she came back, I asked her if she'd brought the lotion, and she said it was in one of the two shopping bags which she'd just **hauled** into the house. She held out a bag to me which was almost bursting at the **seams**, and I quickly took out what looked like suntan lotion."

"But it wasn't?"

"No, it was mayonnaise. But I only **realised** that when I started rubbing it into Sven's back. It didn't soak into the skin at all. Then Sven took the tube out of my hand and made some comment about how I should know by now that he prefers ketchup."

"Well, that makes the situation crystal clear. Now you know why he dumped you." Lucilla nodded, her mind at rest.

"That wasn't it," I said.

"Wasn't he angry?"

"Man, Lucilla, it was an accident! Sven laughed his head off and said that was typical Jojo. Only I could do something as stupid as that. The only bad thing was that we then both **got sunburnt**, but there are creams for that."

"Oh well, maybe he's just waiting for the sunburn to go before he calls you."

---

to haul – schleppen; seam – Naht;
to realise – merken;
to get sunburnt – Sonnenbrand kriegen

"But that was two days ago. Two valuable days of holiday!" I grumbled.

"Maybe there's a completely different explanation," suggested Lucilla.

"Oh, and what then, please?"

By now we'd got to the ice-cream parlour. We were about to go in when Lucilla grabbed my arm and pulled me back.

"Oh my God, it's Sven!" she cried.

"It can't be!" I **peered** cautiously into the ice-cream parlour. "You're right! Sven's sitting there! With *two* girls!"

Lucilla held up her hand to her mouth, shocked. "**Sheez**! That's probably why he hasn't called you."

"No," I said after thinking for a second. "*Two* girls are OK. It would be worse if it was *one* girl."

Lucilla nodded. "True." Then she added, "Unless he hasn't **decided** yet."

"Decided what?"

"You know – which one to take. Maybe one of them is just a **back-up** if the girl he chooses says no."

"What are you talking about?" I snapped.

"About Sven's new girlfriend," replied Lucilla as if it were the most natural thing in the world.

---

to peer – spähen;
sheez – sinngemäß: oh nein!;
to decide – sich entscheiden;
back-up – Reserve

I looked at her **furiously**. Then I turned around and ran home.

My holidays were ruined. I might as well have just kept going to school – that couldn't be any more depressing than what I'd just seen with my very own eyes.

Thursday 10th July

"Jojo, wake up! You can't just sleep through a whole precious day of the holidays!" someone called from the corridor.

Sometimes my mum is in an unbearably good mood. Besides, I don't want to sleep through the holidays; I want to sleep through the rest of my life!

"Aren't you going to get up?" she enquired.

"No!"

That's plenty of information. Simple question, simple answer.

But then Mum came into the room. I **withdrew** under my **pillow.**

"But Jojo," said Mum as she sat down next to me on the bed. "I expect you've got all sorts of plans with Sven. So, come on, **rise and shine!**"

---

furiously – wütend;
to withdraw – sich verziehen;
pillow – Kissen;
rise and shine! – raus aus den Federn!

"I don't want to," I mumbled from underneath the pillow.

"If I were you, I wouldn't leave Sven waiting so long. Who knows, he might start looking elsewhere."

"Can't you go and **bug** Flippi instead?" I shouted from under my pillow.

"Jojo, what's the matter with you?" asked Mum, patting my pillow, alarmed.

"Nothing!" I **sobbed**. "I just want to be left in peace!"

"Alright then." Mum stood up and added, "But if you want to talk about it..."

"No!"

No way. Mum would make me a cup of tea, and we'd settle down to have a little chat and solve my problems. That was the last thing I could do with now.

Mum left the room. At last.

Can't anyone be left in peace to **suffer** alone in this house?

Soon afterwards the door opened and my annoying little sister Flippi came in and dropped down onto my bed. Great. Are there no other seating possibilities in this house apart from my bedside?

---

to bug – nerven;
to sob – schluchzen;
to suffer – leiden

"Now listen up," she got straight to the point. "I'm planning on creating a new **breed** of **snail**, and you're going to help me. As an expert, so to speak," said Flippi **sternly**.

I peered out from under my pillow. "Get out!" I **bawled** at her.

"Wait a second. You get the prototype, and you can even keep him. What do you think about snails for people in love?" she asked, dying to see my reaction.

I sobbed out loud. "Can't you all just leave me in peace?" I yelled and jumped out of bed.

I **dragged** Flippi off the edge of my bed, pushed her out of my room, slammed the door and leant against it.

Flippi was so surprised that she even forgot to defend herself. It was only when she found herself outside of the room that she **grasped** what had just happened and started hammering against the door.

"You chicken brain, you've **lost your marbles**! I even wanted to give you a share of my profits. I might even have made you an equal partner. But you can forget it now. And you'd better lock the door," she **threatened**.

---

breed – Zucht; snail – Schnecke; sternly – streng;
to bawl – anschnauzen; to drag – zerren;
to grasp – begreifen;
to have lost one's marbles – nicht mehr alle Tassen im Schrank haben; to threaten – drohen

Of course, that was the answer.

"I was just about to!" I shouted through the door and fumbled for the key.

Damn! Where was the key? I had to lock the door urgently. Flippi was **no sissy** when it came to **acts of vengeance**. As I couldn't find the key, I had no other choice but to drag my desk in front of the door.

Just to make things crystal clear, I quickly called out into the corridor, "And just so you all know: I'm never ever going to leave my room again. I'm going to stay here until I'm old and grey. So kindly accept that! No one is ever going to come in through this door again."

So, now we can finally get some peace.

Then I threw myself back into bed and pulled the covers over my head.

All of a sudden someone knocked at my window. Oskar was standing on a **ladder** outside my window, waving at me. He had a cup of tea in his hand.

I opened the window. "What's up?"

"Hello, Jojo, your mum said I should bring you a cup of tea." Oskar handed me the cup. "Can I come in?"

I thought about it for a second. Since he was

---

to be no sissy – nicht zimperlich sein;
act of vengeance – Racheaktion;
ladder – Leiter

here, I might as well talk to him. At the end of the day, Oskar was the most **reasonable** member of our family – which probably had something to do with the fact that he wasn't related to us. He was just Mum's boyfriend. My dad had **legged it** when Flippi was still in **nappies**, and Oskar had been a part of our family for a while – for which he should be awarded a **bravery medal**. You see, I'm not all that complicated, but Flippi is a **public nuisance**, and my mother – whoa – God only knows how complicated she is.

Maybe I should let him in. Oskar would probably be able to restore my **confidence**. Then I'd feel better.

"Come in," I growled.

Oskar clambered in through the window and took the cup of tea back out of my hand. Then he took a look around my room and eventually sat down on the chair at my desk. That spoke for him. At last someone who didn't immediately sit on my bed.

I was a bit confused by the fact he'd taken the tea away from me. Actually, I quite fancied a cup of tea.

Oskar took a sip. I looked at him **in dismay**. Hey, that was my tea!

---

reasonable – vernünftig; to leg it – die Fliege machen; nappies – Windeln; bravery medal – Tapferkeitsmedaille; public nuisance – Landplage; confidence – Zuversicht; in dismay – missbilligend

"Did you just come here to drink tea?" I snapped at him.

"No, I just thought I'd come by in case you wanted to talk to someone."

"I don't want to talk to anyone!" To give **emphasis** to my words I stalked back to my bed and slipped under the covers.

Oskar nodded. "OK, fine." He took another sip of tea.

Now that was going too far. I'd force him to talk to me!

I sat up. "Oskar, you're a boy… er, I mean… a man. Well, just imagine you were in love with a girl, what would you do?"

The question seemed to put Oskar **under enormous strain**. "Yes… well… I'd tell her."

I **waved** at him **dismissively**. "Yeah, yeah. I don't mean that. What else would you do?"

Oskar pulled a helpless face again. He had no idea where to begin. "Can I go wrong with my answer?" he asked cautiously.

"No."

"Hm. What would I do if I was in love? Oh, I know. I'd invite the lady to dinner."

I shook my head. "I don't mean that either."

"What do you mean then?"

---

emphasis – Nachdruck;
under enormous strain – leicht überfordert;
to wave dismissively – abwinken

"OK, what I really mean is: what *wouldn't* you do?"

That didn't seem to help him either. "Jojo," he said, almost **beseeching** me, "I think it would be a lot better if you just said what this is about. Ask me a concrete question."

"OK. If you were in love with a girl, would there be any reason not to call her? Neither call her nor visit her, or anything else?"

Oskar laughed. "No, that would **hardly** be a sign of my love."

I burst into tears.

It was as clear as day: Sven didn't love me anymore! I cried and cried and couldn't stop.

Oskar was **at the end of this tether**. "Did I say something wrong, Jojo? I can think about it again, if you like."

"No, it's OK, but I'd like to be alone now."

Oskar nodded, overcome with **remorse**, and he glanced from my barricaded door to the window for a moment. After letting out a sigh, he clambered out of the window, leaving the cup of tea behind. It was now empty.

For a while I had some peace and quiet until I heard someone murmuring in the corridor.

---

to beseech – anflehen; hardly – kaum;
at the end of this tether – fix und fertig;
remorse – Reue

"Oh, hello, Sven," I heard Flippi say in front of my door. "Who are the flowers for?"

Sven? With flowers?

"No. There's no chance, Sven. Jojo doesn't want to see anybody. She won't even come out of her room."

What? Is she crazy? Sven with flowers? And she wants to send him away?

I tore the desk away from my bedroom door in record time and rushed out.

But I only stumbled into Flippi, Mum and Oskar, waiting in front of my room.

"That's the way to do it," said Flippi **haughtily** as she turned on her heels.

Oskar just about managed to hold me back before I **charged at** Flippi and tried to **strangle** her.

"You're **mean**! You're all so mean!" I shrieked.

Flippi turned to Mum and Oskar. "I only said I'd get her out of her room. You're **responsible** for the rest." Then she went.

I dramatically declared that I would now **move** to Lucilla's. She'd let me suffer in peace. Then I

---

haughtily – überheblich;
to charge at sb – auf jmdn. losgehen;
to strangle – erwürgen; mean – gemein;
responsible – verantwortlich;
to move – hier: umziehen

went back into my room. I would now get dressed and walk past Mum and Oskar with my head held high to leave the house without saying another word. Yes, that's what I would do. As soon as I found a black T-shirt. Because I would probably never wear bright colours ever again.

Thursday evening 10th July

Unfortunately, I only had one single black T-shirt and – **Sod's Law** – it had *don't worry, be happy* written on it. What a disaster! But I couldn't be all that **choosy**.

On the way to Lucilla's I got really worked up about my family. For all their efforts to try and cheer me up, I hadn't had any time to suffer! I'm going through the biggest drama of my life, and I wasn't even getting anything out of it!

Why can't I just be in a bad mood? In my opinion, teenagers have a fundamental right to be in a bad mood. There must be some **law** to prevent family members from forcing their **relatives** to be in a good mood.

As I stomped along in my bad mood, I went through my last meeting with Sven in my mind.

Sod's Law – unglücklicherweise;
choosy – wählerisch; law – Gesetz;
relatives – Verwandte

Something must have happened which made him never want to talk to me again.

There was the episode with the fried sausage, the mishap with the mayonnaise, and we talked about being romantic or something.

Oh no! That could be it!

I had complained about Sven being so unromantic. I'd told him our relationship would be absolutely perfect if it could just be a bit more romantic.

"You think it's unromantic if I catch a fried sausage for you?" Sven asked with a grin.

"You see, that's what I mean," I'd said. "That's not romantic; it's **silly**."

Sven didn't seem too happy about my point of view. "Then get me an **instruction manual** on being romantic, and I'll put on a bit of romance for you. Do you want me to write you a poem or sing you a serenade under your balcony? Ignoring the fact that you don't actually have a balcony."

"If I have to tell you what to do, then it's not romantic anymore. You have to surprise me!" I explained to him, feeling **annoyed**.

I probably should have ended the discussion at that point, but unfortunately, I didn't. I said something about being romantic was always proof

---

silly – albern;
instruction manual – Bedienungsanleitung;
annoyed – verärgert

of someone's love, to which Sven mumbled "**rubbish**" and hardly talked to me anymore.

That was it! I'd scared him off with my stupid romantic **whinging**.

I turned into the street where Lucilla lived and saw her coming towards me, waving a piece of paper.

Lucilla gave me a hug and **brandished** the piece of paper cheerfully. "I've got everything under control. Come on, let's go through the list."

"Hey, wait a second. How did you know I was coming?"

"Your mum called me and told me. She told me to be nice to you and look after you!"

"Man! I hate her! Why does she have to do things like that?"

"Because she cares about you," said Lucilla without even thinking about it for a second, and she held the piece of paper under my nose.

"What's that?"

Lucilla **beamed**. "A list of boys who **come into consideration**."

"Into consideration for what?"

"You know, as Sven's **successor**."

I howled out loud.

---

rubbish – Quatsch; whinging – Gejammer;
to brandish – schwenken; to beam – strahlen;
to come into consideration – in Frage kommen;
successor – Nachfolger

Lucilla **faltered**. "You don't like the idea?"

"No!"

Lucilla shrugged her shoulders. "I just wanted to help you."

"If you want to help me, then call Sven and ask him what's going on."

Lucilla **hummed and hawed**, and then she mumbled, "I already did."

"So?" I asked with panic in my voice.

"He **fobbed me off**. 'I haven't got any time. I'm busy,' he said."

"Why didn't you demand an explanation from him?"

"I did, but he just said he didn't want to say anything, because I would probably go and tell you straight away."

Now my nerves were completely in shreds. "This looks like it's the first case ever of somebody dumping their partner but wanting to keep it a secret from them," I **blubbered**.

Lucilla looked at me **compassionately**. "It's really tough, Jojo. I feel so sorry for you."

I sniffled. Lucilla was desperately trying to think of something.

---

to falter – stocken;
to hum and haw – herumdrucksen;
to fob off sb – jmd. abspeisen;
to blubber – schluchzen;
compassionately – mitleidig

"What about if you just pretended you didn't know he'd dumped you?"

I looked at her, **contemplating** the suggestion. "Do you think that could work?"

Lucilla shrugged her shoulders. "It's worth a try."

We walked along side by side for a while in silence. Then Lucilla said, "Come on, give him a call!"

"No!"

"But you can't just accept the situation as it is! OK, maybe he really does want to dump you – but at least he's got to tell you!"

Lucilla had a good point there.

All of a sudden, I felt my **fighting spirit** surging up in me again. I wouldn't just let Sven go without a struggle. Oh no, I'd fight for him! Or in other words, Lucilla would fight for him.

"I've got it: you can **shadow** Sven!" I exclaimed with newly-found courage.

"I don't know..." Lucilla didn't seem to be too **keen** on the idea.

"Yes, you do. Just stick to his heels and let me know what he's up to every hour!"

"Alright then, but only if you come with me."

"But that's the point, I don't want him to see me. He knows me."

---

to contemplate – nachdenken;
fighting spirit – Kampfgeist;
to shadow sb – jmdn. beschatten;
to be keen on sth – auf etwas scharf sein

"So? He knows me, too!"

"OK, then forget the plan. Have you got another idea?"

Lucilla thought for a moment. "Yes. You start making a mental list of why it's better not to be together with Sven anymore," she suggested.

"What for?"

"You know, just in case it really is over. Then you can even be happy about it."

I looked at Lucilla, **dumbfounded**. There's no way I could ever, ever be happy about that.

"It's just a safety precaution," Lucilla tried to **temper her words**. "Come on, let's go for a walk in the park, and you can think about it."

I didn't want to go for a walk, so I suggested to Lucilla that we make ourselves **comfortable** on a bench in the sun. I could think better sitting down.

"Alright then, but I hope you've got some mayonnaise with you," Lucilla giggled. "The sun is burning hot, and I don't want to get sunburnt!"

"Ha, ha! Really funny," I **growled** angrily. Then I tried to concentrate.

I looked into the distance and thought about why it could be good if Sven dumped me.

---

dumbfounded – entgeistert;
to temper one's words – eine Äußerung abmildern;
comfortable – gemütlich;
to growl – knurren

After three hours I still didn't have a single argument. There wasn't one.

Oh, what a **nightmare**!

Friday 11th July

After Lucilla and I spent yesterday looking at my situation from every possible angle, we decided it was a hopeless case and that I'd be better off spending a few days actively engaging myself in the art of suffering. At home. In my room – which I would never leave again until I was an adult. Or at least until the holidays were over. Meanwhile Lucilla would take care of shadowing Sven.

I'd only just settled down in bed when Lucilla called to make her first **report**.

She'd followed Sven to the supermarket, a flower shop, a bookshop (the cook book section), and – oh, **woe is me**! – had seen him in the ice-cream parlour with the same two girls as before, deep in conversation. I'd finally had enough. Sven owed me an answer. I instructed Lucilla to **hunt down** Sven and demand an explanation.

Lucilla had the crazy idea I should do it myself! I really don't know what goes on in her head some-

---

nightmare – Albtraum; report – Bericht;
woe is me! – wehe mir!;
to hunt down – zur Rede stellen

times. Talk about absurd! After all, we'd both decided that I should never leave my room again. It's difficult to deal with your life when you're stuck in a room of four by six metres.

I told Lucilla that I would have to **reconsider** the part of our plan about spending the rest of my life in my room.

"Good idea," she said. "I'm going to the pool now. It's boiling hot today. Let me know what you decide."

"How am I meant to do that if you're at the pool?" I grumbled, annoyed that my best friend would be hanging out at the pool while I had to **squat** around here in my room.

"I'll give you a call tonight."

"And what if I decide earlier?"

"Then just come around to the pool."

"Never!"

"Alright then," she said, "I'll give you a call every two hours and get an **update** from you. OK?"

Why is everything always so simple for Lucilla?

My life was one big disaster. This was my painful realisation as Flippi appeared in my room all of a sudden.

---

to reconsider – überdenken;
to squat – hocken;
update – neuester Bericht

"Have you ever thought about knocking?" I **snapped at her**.

"Waste of time," was all Flippi could say to that. Then she pushed a box over to me. "Here, that's for you. It's a new breed. A **lovesick** snail. It's bound to help."

"A lovesick snail?"

"Yeah, she can keep you company while you sit in your room. And she'll always have an ear for you. But don't overdo it. She might need a break at some point, too."

I was touched. "That's really ni..." I just managed to stop myself. If there's one thing that Flippi **can't stand**, it's being called nice or sweet. She gave me a look of warning. I patted Flippi on the shoulder. "You know what I mean... Thanks."

"It's alright. Oskar gave me five euros for it," she explained.

My touched emotions disappeared **in a flash**.

"But now you have to take her for a walk. She needs fresh air and exercise," said Flippi.

"What? I thought she was meant to **keep** me **company**."

"Yes, but she also needs a change of air occa-

---

to snap at sb – jmdn. anfauchen;
to be lovesick – Liebeskummer haben;
to stand sth – etwas ertragen;
in a flash – auf der Stelle;
to keep company – Gesellschaft leisten

sionally. The best place for her is the swimming pool…"

I looked at Flippi **suspiciously**. "Oskar offered you a bonus if you got me to leave my room, right?"

Flippi nodded.

"Forget it," I barked at her, pointing to the door.

Flippi walked out of my room, leaving me behind with a snail in a box.

I opened the box and looked at the snail.

"Hello, I'm Jojo," I **introduced myself**. "And I've got problems with my boyfriend, but you'll probably be hearing a lot more about that."

Hey, just a moment, why am I pouring out my heart to some snail? Oh, my God! I've gone mad. And it's all Sven's fault. And why hasn't Lucilla given me a call?

Then the phone rang! At last, at last, at last!

Wait! Stop! Don't answer the phone. It wouldn't do any harm to Lucilla if she was left to worry about me for a bit. Leaving me here all on my own like that.

I opened the door and called out into the corridor. "I'm not here. Whoever it is. OK?"

"OK," three voices echoed back.

Ha! That would teach Lucilla.

---

suspiciously – misstrauisch;
to introduce oneself – sich vorstellen

But then my curiosity **got the better of me**, and I poked my head around the door five minutes later. "So? What did Lucilla want?"

"It wasn't Lucilla," replied Flippi.

I slammed my bedroom door shut again. Well, great. She'd already forgotten about me. She was amusing herself at the pool while I was just sitting here and...

My door opened. Flippi poked her head in and said, "You should go to the park tomorrow afternoon at five o'clock."

"Lucilla **can take a running jump**!" I cursed. "She can go for a walk in the park on her own."

"Or she can meet up with Sven. He called and wanted to speak with you. He wants to meet you tomorrow in the park."

"Sven!!!" I shrieked hysterically. "Sven! Why didn't anyone let me know it was him? Why didn't someone tell me to come to the phone?"

Flippi rolled her eyes and called into the corridor, "Mum, I think it's finally happened: she's off her rocker. Do we really have to keep her here? There are really **great homes**."

"Flippi, be quiet!" Mum appeared in the doorway, shoved Flippi back into the corridor and

---

to get the better of sb – jmdn. überwältigen, stärker sein;
she can take a running jump! –
sie kann mir gestohlen bleiben!;
great homes – tolle Pflegeheime

smiled at me warmly. "See? There you are... Everything's going to be alright. I'd already guessed something was up with Sven..."

"Just leave me alone!" I cut short Mum in a **whingy** voice.

"OK, OK," she said, nodding her head. "If you want a chat or a cup of tea... you know... anytime!"

She carefully closed the door behind her, and her endless compassion only made me more furious. But I had no time **to dwell on** my mum. First, I had to deal with Sven's call. Unfortunately, I wasn't able to feel particularly overjoyed about it. I still had a **lump** in my throat. And probably **rightly so**.

Sven had asked me to come to the park tomorrow afternoon. Was that a good sign? If everything was like it was before, then he would have just come around and asked me. He wouldn't have called and left a message. So: no. Not a good sign.

I swallowed. He wanted to dump me in public. He probably just wanted to avoid a scene and thought it would be too embarrassing for me to cry or **have a go at him** in public.

Well, he was wrong there!

On the other hand... maybe I should play it

---

whingy – jammernd;
to to dwell on sb/sth – sich aufhalten mit jmdm./etwas;
lump – Kloß; rightly so – zu Recht;
to have a go at sb – auf jmdn. losgehen

really cool, as if I couldn't care less. That was it! I'd listen to what he had to say with complete **indifference**.

Or I could dump him myself. As soon as I saw him I could smile coolly and tell him that, unfortunately, I didn't have any time for him anymore and that it would be better if we **called it a day**. Then I'd turn around and leave. I could **bawl** my eyes out at home.

Exactly. That was the best idea.

After I'd settled on my plan, I cried a bit. Well, not exactly a bit: I absolutely bawled my eyes out.

Saturday 12th July

Lucilla called me yesterday evening at last and urgently recommended that I end my **self-inflicted incarceration**. The weather was just too good, and there was a lot going on at the pool, and the summer and the holidays had only just begun. And anyway, I should put things with Sven behind me and get on with my life. When I told her that I was going to meet Sven in the park, she said that – strictly speaking – it would be great if he dumped

---

indifference – Gleichgültigkeit;
to call it a day – Schluss machen;
to bawl – heulen;
self-inflicted incarceration – selbst auferlegter Arrest

me there. After all, I was still so young, and there were so many other nice boys around.

Normally, I'd have disagreed with her, of course, because Sven is by far the nicest boy I've ever met. But under the current circumstances I wasn't **feeling** quite so **enamoured with** him as normal. The plan was to make a really cool **exit** in the park so that Sven deeply regretted ever even having thought about dumping me.

We had a step-by-step plan of how I should go about it. I would go to the park fifteen minutes later than requested, just to make him wait. Then I wouldn't even let him get a word out; I'd just say in a voice as sweet as sugar, "Hi, Sven, nice of you to wait. And while we're on the subject of waiting, I just wanted to let you know: you needn't wait for me anymore in the future, because I won't have any time for you. To be precise, I won't have any time at all. But don't take it too hard, you're **bound to** find another nice girl."

Then I'd turn around and **strut off** in the best of moods. The plan was good.

The fact that I ended up arriving fifteen minutes early, and had to wait impatiently for Sven in front

---

to feel enamoured with sb – von jmdm. begeistert sein;
exit – hier: Abgang;
to be bound to – etwas bestimmt tun/werden;
to strut off – davonstolzieren

of the park, meant the plan started **on the wrong foot**, of course.

Sven came up to me with a big smile on his face. Fantastic! He was actually happy to be **getting rid of me**. He even had a rose in his hand. I see, now it's all over he starts putting on the romance.

As he went to kiss me, I turned my face to the side.

"Nice of you to wait," I started my planned speech.

"What do you mean?" asked Sven.

What a **botch**! Of course that didn't make sense anymore. I had to improvise.

"You wanted to talk to me?" I asked coolly.

Sven grinned. "Not so much talk to you, I wanted to show you something. Come with me."

I held up my **wrist** to look **tediously** at my watch. "I haven't got much time."

Sven pointed at my wrist. "Yeah, and you haven't got a watch on either."

I looked again at my wrist. Damn, Sven was right.

"I always tell the time by looking at my wrist. I'm highly **proficient**." Just don't show any weak points. Everything was going well until now.

"Here," said Sven, handing me the rose. Then he

---

to start on the wrong foot – schlecht anfangen;
to get rid of sb – jmdn. loswerden; botch – Murks;
wrist – Handgelenk; tediously – gelangweilt;
to be proficient – etwas gut können

pointed to the grass. "You just have to follow the roses."

I was amazed by what I saw: there were roses **dotted** about the grass in a line. They stretched over the lawn like a path, past a big fat tree and ended in a **hedgerow**.

OK. He'd obviously come up with a very extravagant way of dumping me. I sighed. Sven was sooo sweet.

But I just wanted to get it over and done with at last.

As I walked along the path of roses, I said, "Somebody I know saw you hanging out with two girls recently."

It wouldn't do him any harm to know that nothing was a secret to me. Would he **deny** it?

Sven nodded. "Yeah, I needed a few tips."

I held my breath. That's unbelievable! He doesn't even have the **decency** to try and talk his way out of it. Tips? Huh, that was original! He was getting tips on how to dump someone! Had the man no shame?

"Good, then let's get it over and done with." I stomped along.

"Hey, saying 'let's get it over and done with' isn't

---

dotted – verstreut;
hedgerow – Hecke;
to deny – abstreiten;
decency – Anstand

exactly putting me in a good mood!" grumbled Sven.

"Well, great, **that makes two of us**."

Sven stopped in his tracks. "Hey, Jojo, is something the matter?"

I **snorted scornfully**. The guy really had a nerve. "Everything's just fine," I called over my shoulder to him and **trudged** on.

The track of roses ended in a large hedge. I fought my way through its branches and was almost **bowled over** by what I saw on the other side.

Behind the hedge was a table covered in a long, white tablecloth and a silver **candelabrum** with five arms. There were rose petals scattered on the table. It was **classily** laid for two people, with expensive porcelain, cloth serviettes and all.

Meanwhile Sven had also crawled through the hedge and was standing next to me. He was looking at me slightly **irritably**.

"For you," he said **gruffly**, pointing at the table.

I **gulped**. "Well, marvellous," I said furiously. "Why didn't you ever do something like this when we were still together?"

---

that makes two of us – da sind wir ja zu zweit;
to snort scornfully – verächtlich schnauben;
to trudge – stapfen;
to bowl over – umwerfen;
candelabrum – Leuchter;
classily – edel; irritably – verärgert;
gruffly – mürrisch; to gulp – schlucken

"I beg your pardon?" asked Sven.

I had tears in my eyes. "It's sooo romantic!" I sobbed.

Sven grabbed me by the arm and pulled me close. "Something's not right here," he said, looking me in the eyes. "Would you **mind** telling me what you're talking about?"

It couldn't go on like this. I couldn't be bothered with Sven's fun and games any more. I'd now **tell him to his face** what was wrong.

"You didn't call for five days," I started. "And you were **having a whale of a time** with those other girls. And I know it's sometimes hard work being friends with me – well, at least that's what my mum says – but there's only one thing that really interests me: do you just need a break or is it over once and for all?"

I had to gulp loudly during my speech, but I was really proud of myself that I didn't start to cry.

Sven put his hand on my shoulder and looked me in the eyes. "Hey, you're not crying, are you?"

"No, I've got an allergy and, besides, something just flew into my eye. Don't **get it into your head** I'm crying about you. I don't care if you dump me!"

Sven looked at me completely dumbfounded.

---

to mind – etwas dagegen haben;
to tell sb sth to his face – jmdm. etwas auf den Kopf zusagen;
having a whale of a time – jede Menge Spaß haben;
to get it into one's head – sich etwas einbilden

Then he started to laugh. "I don't believe it!" he snorted with laughter. "That's typical Jojo again!"

I kept quiet, still feeling hurt.

Sven stopped laughing and took me in his arms. "You complained I wasn't romantic enough, so I really made an effort to put on some romance for you. I asked some experts from my class, and they helped me with this idea. I think it's all a bit silly really, but my team of experts said you'd be guaranteed to melt in my arms when you saw it."

I looked at him in disbelief. "Does that mean it's not over?"

"Of course not! The things you get into your head! Your brain should have warning signs!"

"Well, I never..."

Sven quickly kissed me so that I couldn't say anything else.

Oh, I was happy! And then we sat down at the beautiful table.

"Is there something to eat as well?" I asked.

"What do you think? I prepared everything personally. It was a lot of work."

Sven bent down under the table, but jumped straight back up in shock. He looked to the left and right in a panic, ran through the hedge and back, looked at the table again, then underneath it, looked into his empty hands and in the end **groaned**, "Oh,

---

to groan – stöhnen

my God! I left the food at home! Or it's still in the car. My dad drove me here to bring all this stuff over, and I must have left behind the basket of food somewhere! Somewhere – just not here, unfortunately. I can't believe it!"

I giggled.

"I've **got it from you**!" cursed Sven.

I nodded. "That's just what I thought!"

Sven was still looking quite annoyed, but I couldn't be anything other than in an extremely good mood. Sven and I were still together; I didn't care about anything else. And from now on being romantic wouldn't matter to me either. Although this here was absolutely mega-romantic. I could get used to this.

"And what are we going to do now?" I asked, laughing.

Sven shrugged his shoulders. "I'll get two portions of **chips** from the **chippie**, and then we can eat them."

"I looove chips!"

Sven smiled. He was in a better mood already. "I've got something else for you," he said. "You're not really meant to get it until dessert, but as our three-course menu has been **turned on its head**...

---

to get it from sb – sich bei jmdm. anstecken;
chips – Pommes;
chippie – Frittenbude;
to turn sth on its head – etwas total durcheinander bringen

Here…" Sven reached into his trouser pocket and pulled out a stack of photos.

Each photo showed Sven holding up a large letter into the air.

I looked at him curiously.

Sven grinned. "You just have to put the photos in the right order to get a message!"

Hey, that was exciting. I set about my task at once. It was a **cinch**.

"*Yeliou,*" I cried. "But I've still got an 'o' and a 'v' left over." Then I looked at Sven. "What's that supposed to mean?"

Sven rolled his eyes. "It means you haven't got the letters in the right order."

Oh, right. Then try again. It was much harder than I thought.

Iouley? Again an 'o' and a 'v' were left over. Wrong answer.

Ieoul? This time a 'y' added itself to the usual 'o' and 'v'.

Sven sighed, got up and helped me. He spread the photos out on the table in the right order. Oh, right, that made sense.

Smiling from ear to ear, I read the message out loud: "*I love you*!"

Sven grinned. "I **guessed** that already, but I'm glad you **admit** it."

---

cinch – Kleinigkeit, Kinderspiel;
to guess – raten, vermuten; to admit – zugeben

"Oh, Sven!" I whinged. "You're being unromantic again!"

And I was a bit angry. But only a **teeny-weeny bit,** of course.

No, actually, I wasn't angry at all.

---

a teeny-weeny bit – ein winzig kleines bisschen

Irene Zimmermann

Love, Frustration & Birthday Elation

"Happy birthday, Tanja!" cried Mum and Simon. The two of them were standing at my bedroom door, carrying a birthday cake with fourteen pink candles. "Happy birthday!"

I sat up in bed sleepily.

"Come on! Blow out the candles! All of them at once, **mind you**, otherwise it brings bad luck," said my brother. "I messed it up last year, and the following day I **dented** the car. And then there was the time…"

"Stop trying to **scare** Tanja," protested Mum. She held the cake right under my nose. "Come on, give it your best! And remember: whatever you wish will come true."

I closed my eyes and concentrated. Then I blew out the candles.

Simon laughed as he gave me my birthday present. "I've got the feeling your wish is just about to come true: they didn't have the earrings in red any-

---

mind you – denk daran;
to dent – etwas einbeulen;
to scare – ängstigen

more, but I thought turquoise would **suit** you, too. If you don't like them, then we can change them."

"And from me you get the necklace **to go with it**," said Mum. "I just haven't **got around to** ordering it yet." She leaned forward and gave me a hug. "Tanja, I really feel bad about leaving you all on your own today, but it'll be really great if I do get the **lease** for the sports restaurant. Simon will be able to work there and..."

"Just **keep your fingers crossed** for us," said Simon. "We'll be home at eight thirty at the latest, and then we can really **push the boat out**, OK? Is Henri coming this afternoon?"

I shook my head. "She's going to Düsseldorf with her family. Her grandparents are celebrating their **golden wedding anniversary** tomorrow, but we'll definitely meet up next week."

Mum hesitated. "Are you sure we can leave you on your own? On your birthday?"

I laughed. "Of course, you can. I'll just have another **nap**, and after that I can watch a bit of TV or something. Don't you worry about me!"

---

to suit sb – jmdm. gut stehen;
to go with it – dazu passend;
to get around to do sth – dazu kommen, etwas zu tun;
to lease sth – pachten;
keep your fingers crossed – drück die Daumen;
to push the boat out – ausgelassen feiern;
golden wedding anniversary – goldene Hochzeit;
nap – Nickerchen

"Oh, by the way!" Mum turned around again in the doorway. "I put the weekly horoscope on the kitchen table for you." She **winked** at me. "It's perfect, Tanja. You were really **born under a lucky star**, believe me!"

Ten minutes later I heard them leaving the flat. Originally, I'd planned to sleep until at least midday every day in the holidays, but it was **a bit of a shame** to do that on my birthday. So I got up, went into the kitchen, and took a look at my horoscope.

You're a child of fortune, I read. *Important changes are on the horizon. Change yourself, too, and nothing will stand in the way of your happiness.*

That sounded pretty good. Not some disaster or anything like that. Not like last week when my horoscope made prophecies about *surprises,* and then **out of the blue** we had to sit an English exam in school.

It was a bit annoying that the horoscope didn't actually say what the changes were, but maybe I would soon no longer belong to the few people in the class who didn't have a boyfriend! I sighed as I poured myself a glass of milk.

---

to wink – zwinkern;
to be born under a lucky star – ein Glückskind/Sonntagskind sein;
a bit of a shame – eigentlich schade;
out of the blue – ohne Vorwarnung

I decided I'd better take the thing about change literally. The dark red colour of my hair – which I'd had for the past two months – really didn't match the fantastic earrings which Simon had given me. Instead of changing the earrings, I would just change the colour of my hair!

Mum still had some **hair bleach** in the bathroom, so I decided I'd become blonde. I smeared the stuff into my hair, covered it with a plastic bag to intensify the blonde colour, and wrapped a towel around my head. Then I set the alarm clock in the kitchen for twenty-five minutes later.

With the turban on my head, I cut a **slice** of my birthday cake and tried the first piece. I wondered if blowing out all the candles with a wish would actually help.

I'd better **play it safe**.

I carefully locked my bedroom door – there wasn't actually anyone in the flat apart from me, but you never know – and then unlocked the **drawer** in my desk. I carried the key for it on a ribbon around my neck.

No one should ever catch me doing what I was about to do now.

I put on my favourite CD, muttered an African spell, lit three candles – it was at least thirty degrees

---

hair bleach – Blondierungsmittel; slice – Scheibe;
to play it safe – auf Nummer sicher gehen;
drawer – Schublade

in my room, but certain **sacrifices** had to be made so that the whole thing had an effect – and then came the big moment.

I opened the silver **cardboard box**, which I had lined with rose **petals**, and took out a picture.

I was so madly in love with David!

It had cost me a lot of trouble to get my hands on that picture. I knew Heike, his elder sister, vaguely from volleyball, and at some point I'd **bumped into** her on the street just as she was coming out of a photo shop. It seemed she'd just picked up her holiday photos, and she stopped on the **pavement** outside to flick through them with a **frown** on her face. I pulled up right next to her on my bike and acted as if I were her best friend.

If she was at all surprised by my behaviour, she certainly didn't show it.

"**Turkey**," she said, holding an overexposed photo under my nose. "Look at him, the guy at the front with the red baseball cap. That's Marcel. **Cute**, isn't he? I met him on a **diving course**, and he said..."

---

sacrifice – Opfer;
cardboard box – Pappkarton;
petal – Blütenblatt;
to bump into sb – jmdn. zufällig treffen;
pavement – Bürgersteig; frown – Stirnrunzeln;
Turkey – Türkei; cute – süß;
diving course – Tauchkurs

I patiently listened to fourteen days of holiday **antics** in Turkey with Marcel. Sometimes you just have to invest something to get what you want. And sometimes that thing is time and **patience**. I was quite sure that, at some point, David would be in one of the photos.

By around the thirty-second picture my breath really did come to a halt: David! With a slightly sunburnt nose! **Pitch-black** eyes and black curly hair! And he was smiling just as sweetly as I had him in my memory from the school summer party. He'd accidentally stepped on my foot there and apologised... and then it **got me** really **bad**, although we only exchanged two or three sentences in total.

I must have said something, because Heike looked at me in amazement.

"Let me see the photo of you and Marcel in the pool again," I said quickly. "That was a really good one."

Heike said she was going to make a whole load of prints from it and asked me what I thought of the idea of a poster which she could send to Marcel.

"Yeah, cool," I said. "I'm sure Marcel would really like a poster. Why don't you do it straight away?"

Heike raised two fingers into a victory-sign, put

---

antics – Mätzchen; patience – Geduld;
pitch-black – pechschwarz;
sb has got it bad – jmdn. hat's erwischt (total verliebt sein)

the packet of photos into my hand and rushed with her Marcel-and-Heike-in-the-pool photo back into the shop.

My hands were **trembling** slightly as I quickly flicked through the photos. After seemingly endless seconds I found what I was looking for and slipped it into my trouser pocket with surprisingly little evidence of a **guilty conscience**.

Somewhere in the flat a telephone rang. I blew a kiss to the photo and closed my eyes. It was bound to be David. At last he'd felt the **oscillations** of my thoughts and was now calling me. Since I'd seen a programme on television about telepathy a few weeks ago, I'd really started to believe in it. The **spell** was bound to work.

"Tanja Ostertag," I answered.

I was hoping that my voice would sound fantastic – just in case it really was David – but unfortunately, I was completely out of breath at the time. It hadn't been too easy to find the phone.

"Are you in the middle of running a marathon, or what?" asked Henri. "Or are you just getting old? Many happy returns for your birthday, Tanja!"

---

to tremble – zittern;
guilty conscience – schlechtes Gewissen;
oscillations – Schwingungen;
spell – hier: Zauber

"Henri, thanks for calling. The telephone was under a **pile** of clothes..."

"And what are you doing today?"

"Oh, nothing special. Just a bit of this and a bit of that. I might buy something with the money Dad will probably **cough up** for me. Something to wear. Something green. Simon gave me some really great earrings, and I need a top to go with them – just to bring out the full effect. I'm going to take a look in town later and see what I can find."

Henri seemed to spend a moment running a thought through her head. "We're leaving in two hours," she said. "It's a real **pain** that my grandparents have to celebrate this weekend of all weekends. What about if I came around to your place? In a quarter of an hour? Deal?"

I quickly **cleared up** a bit and laid the table for Henri and me. I was just about to get dressed when the door bell rang.

"Tom came with me!" called Henri from the **stairwell**. "He wants to congratulate you, too."

The two came upstairs holding hands, and for a moment I felt a **twinge** of sadness. Why didn't I

---

pile – Haufen;
to cough up (money) – Geld herausrücken;
pain – hier: Mist; to clear up – aufräumen;
stairwell – Treppenhaus;
twinge – Anflug

have a boyfriend who would go through town with me holding hands?

"Stop looking so heartbroken!" laughed Tom, giving me a kiss. "You've still got your best years to come!"

"That's what it said on the calendar today!" Henri winked at me as she gave me a hug. "Can we come in or are you still half under the shower?"

I probably looked a bit **blank**, because she pointed at my head. "You've washed your hair, haven't you?"

I let out a scream and **ripped** the towel and plastic bag off my head. What a **bummer**! For all the spells and telepathy I hadn't heard the **alarm** in the kitchen!

"Oh," muttered Henri, staring at me.

Tom didn't say anything.

I slowly turned around and looked at myself in the **hall** mirror.

Henri took a closer look at my hair. "It'll wash out!"

I shook my head. It was nice of Henri to comfort me, but nothing would come out of this practically white hair – there was just no more colour pigment in it, or whatever the stuff was called.

---

blank – verständnislos;
to rip – reißen;
bummer – Mist; alarm – Wecker;
hall – Flur, Diele

Tom looked completely **at a loss**.

Henri pushed him into the kitchen. "Eat a slice of cake," she murmured, pointing at the dining table. "Tanja needs me right now. If you happen to think of anything that can help us, then let us know. We'll be in the bathroom!"

I spent at least twenty minutes rinsing my hair over the **bathtub**, but there was no point.

"Oh well," said Henri. She'd sat herself down on the **linen chest** and was fiddling nervously with the **bangle** which Tom had given her last year for Christmas. "Oh well!"

I would really have liked to scream, but that wouldn't bring the colour back to my hair.

"White is really 'in' this summer," said Henri. She **eyed me up**. "Honest, it's fashionable, because..." She snorted with laughter. "Don't be angry with me, Tanja, but you just look so funny!"

There was nothing I could do. I had to laugh as well.

"Everything OK again?" called Tom from the hall. "Have you got the colour back in your hair?"

"Everything's just fine." Henri opened the bathroom door slightly. "You can eat another slice of cake. We'll be ready in a minute."

---

at a loss – ratlos; bathtub – Badewanne;
linen chest – Wäschetruhe;
bangle – Armreif;
to eye sb up – jmdn. beäugen

"I'll just have to **dye** it again," I realised. "Do you think we could quickly send Tom to the shops? Mahogany or something?" Originally, I'd wanted to get away from red, but after this experiment I didn't want to take any more risks.

Henri nodded. "Lucky that Tom came with me. I'll tell him to go and buy some mahogany dye. You'd better wash your hair a few more times and get rid of all that bleach. You don't want it to still have an effect... Have you got any money anywhere? I haven't got any with me."

"My purse is in my school bag." I turned the **tap** on full blast and scrubbed at my scalp.

I will never again dye my hair blonde! Red looked quite good actually. How on earth did I come up with the idea of dying my hair a different colour?

And all for David! All because I wanted him to like me!

David!

I shot upright. I ran past the utterly **baffled** Tom with dripping wet hair into my room, but it was too late!

Henri was standing right in front of my desk. She slowly turned around.

"Oh dear," she just said, pointing at David's

---

to dye – färben;
tap – Wasserhahn;
baffled – verdattert

picture on my desk. "Tanja, **you've got it** really bad."

There was no point denying it. First of all, Henri is my best friend, and secondly, the facts spoke for themselves: David's picture in a heart-shaped frame in front of a box of rose petals.

"How long?" asked Henri.

"Since the school party. Exactly three weeks and two days."

Henri stared at the photo and shook her head. "You didn't even **mention** it to me. I didn't even notice anything different about you. I don't get it. I mean, I'm your best friend, aren't I?"

"Of course, you are," I said. "You're my best friend, Henri, but this time... " I sat down on my bed and grabbed the first available **item of clothing** to dry my hair, "... there's nothing to say. I've fallen in love with David, but nothing will **come of it**, because..."

"Because?" Henri looked at me. "Why shouldn't anything come of it? Can you give me one good reason?"

I shrugged my shoulders. It was hot and **stuffy** in the room. I'd liked to have torn open the window, but I knew it wasn't any cooler outside.

---

you've got it – dich hat's erwischt;
to mention – erwähnen;
item of clothing – Kleidungsstück;
to come of it – dabei herauskommen; stuffy – stickig

Henri picked up an old exercise book and started **fanning** herself. "You wanted to give me a good reason why nothing will come of it with David."

"He's so incredibly good-looking, and now look at me." I pointed at my hair. "I haven't got a **hope in hell**."

Henri looked at me. "That's just for the time being. Think about the footballer **calves** I had when I met Tom – and he still thought I was great."

"That's completely different. You can't compare this to you and Tom. I'm sorry, but nothing will come of David. I just know it." I got to my feet, carefully packed away the picture into the box, and put it back in my desk drawer. Then I locked the drawer again. "Besides, I'm probably not his type. I expect he's got a really pretty girlfriend and… he doesn't know I'm in love with him."

Henri laughed. "You're a funny old thing. Don't you know that boys are a bit slower? So you just have to tell him. What's the problem?"

I laughed as well. "I've no idea what the problem is. I could just go to David and say **casually**: 'By the way, did you know that I'm madly in love with you? Why don't we get together?' And then he'd say,

---

to fan – fächern;
no hope in hell – absolut keine Chance;
calves – Waden;
casually – beiläufig

'Sure, of course. Thanks for **pointing** that **out** to me. I'm very grateful to you.'" I shook my head. "Do you seriously think I'd do something like that?"

Henri dropped onto my bed. "Yeah, well, it doesn't have to be quite as **glaringly obvious** as that. There are other possibilities. You're never usually at a loss for words. The way you **made mincemeat of** big-head Rolf at school recently when he made yet another stupid comment – that was really great."

"Yeah, well," I said. How could I explain to Henri that I had no problem **talking the hind legs off** big-head Rolf? I'm also not scared of spiders, like my mum, or of **burglars**, or physics tests. But I'm just absolutely terrified of **being turned down** by David.

"Just talk to him," she repeated. "You can do it, honest. And don't tell me you won't be able to think of anything to say. Really, the things you said to Rolf – that seriously impressed me."

"I can't talk to David," I said quietly. "I'll either turn as red as a **beetroot**, or I'll start **stuttering**, or I'll just **talk rubbish**. Please, don't tell anyone about this, OK? Not even Tom. Promise?"

---

to point out sth – auf etwas hinweisen;
glaringly obvious – allzu offensichtlich;
to make mincemeat of sb – jmdn. zur Schnecke machen;
to talk the hind legs off – jmdn. in Grund und Boden reden;
burglar – Einbrecher; to be turned down – eine Abfuhr bekommen; beetroot – Rote Bete;
to stutter – stottern; to talk rubbish – Quatsch reden

Henri took me in her arms. "Promise," she murmured. "And now we're going to get you a new hair colour. Then everything will work out." She laughed. "I mean, with David!"

Two hours later Henri was at least as much at a loss as I was.

"It must have been some chemical reaction or other. I reckon it had something to do with the oxygen in the air," explained Tom.

Henri rolled her eyes.

"I bought exactly the colour you asked for."

"We could complain to the manufacturers," suggested Henri. "Your hair is now orange red and has a slight **tinge** of green. You could claim **compensation.**"

"**Damages,**" added Tom.

"**Oh man**, Tanja!" said Henri. She looked in a really sorry state. "What are we going to do now?"

I tried to smile. "You have to go. You wanted to go to Düsseldorf today. Don't worry about me. I'll wait here until Mum and Simon come home, and then we're going out for dinner."

"And when will that be?"

"No idea. Sometime this evening. I'll watch a bit

---

tinge – Stich, Anflug;
compensation – Schadensersatz;
damages – hier: Schmerzensgeld;
Oh man! – Mensch!

of TV and think about how I can get another hair colour. Maybe I'll dye it jet black."

"Maybe it would be better if you went to a hairdresser. I reckon it's a job for a professional," said Tom. "Unless you plan to spend the rest of the holidays in your flat."

Henri **nudged** him in the ribs. "**Sheez**, Tom, get off Tanja's back. At least she's got a hair colour that no one else has got."

After the two of them had gone, I piled up the rest of the birthday cake onto a plate and made myself **comfy** on the sofa.

Then I fished out the remote control and, after taking a quick look in the TV guide, I decided to watch a talk show called *I'm alone – so what?*. That seemed **apt** for my day.

The telephone interrupted my lonely birthday party.

"Hello," I asked, somewhat **grumpily**.

I left the TV on because I really wanted to know how Thea from Berlin was coping with the fact that she hadn't had a boyfriend for four months.

"Hello, it's Andreas here. Can you tell me the best way to get to Tanja's? I haven't got an address and..."

---

to nudge – knuffen; sheez – Mist;
comfy – gemütlich;
apt – passend; grumpily – muffig

"To Tanja's? But I'm…"

The boy on the other end of the line sounded a bit embarrassed as he interrupted me. "I've no idea what's happening there either. Some surprise party or something. Tanja hasn't got a **clue**. Lisa, my girlfriend, got a SMS from Henriette from school saying I should call a few more people. Lisa gave me five telephone numbers, and I thought I'd start with you. Maybe you can tell me where Tanja lives."

Brilliant! I almost laughed.

"Yes, I can tell you that," I said and described him the way. "Marien Street 7a. And there's a party there, you say?"

"That's right. It's Tanja's birthday, and the whole thing is meant to be a surprise. Are you coming, too?"

I **hesitated** briefly. "Yes, I probably will. Yes, yes, I'll definitely be there. When does it start? And how many people are coming?"

"It was organised at quite short notice, so not many are coming. Not at the moment anyway. Lisa said something about seventeen or eighteen, but it'll probably be about **twenty-odd** altogether. We're meeting in Marien Street at half past six. Is that OK for you?"

"Just perfect," I said and hung up.

---

clue – hier: Ahnung;
to hesitate – zögern;
twenty-odd – zwanzig und noch was

I'd have to go without Thea and the other lonely hearts. My birthday came first.

A surprise party at half past six, Andreas had said.

I'd already dialled Henri's mobile number, but then I remembered that I wasn't even allowed to know about this party.

"Henri, you're the best friend in the world!" I cried out loudly, hoping that some telepathic oscillations would get to her. Somewhere on the motorway she'd notice how happy I was.

I turned the music on full volume and danced through the living room.

Then I realised that there were a few things I'd have to **arrange**. Officially, I didn't know anything, but I didn't want to stand there completely unprepared. The others were bound to all get **dressed up**.

And what about the colour of my hair?

There was no way I could solve this problem satisfactorily at such short notice, so I just wrapped a light blue batik **scarf** around my head. It suited me actually. Then I stood in front of the wardrobe to a wave of frustration as I realised I had nothing to wear.

I decided to **postpone** the clothes question and

---

to arrange – vorbereiten;
dressed up – schick gemacht;
scarf – Schal; to postpone – vertagen

deal with the more essential problem: what were we going to eat?

So instead of going through my wardrobe I checked out the provisions, but as ever it looked pretty **grim** in that department. Or was it possible to make something to fill up twenty stomachs from three cans of tuna fish, a packet of **ground almonds**, some sliced bread and a jar of olives?

I tried to reach Simon or Mum, but I only got their mailbox.

I'd have to think of something myself as soon as possible.

A brilliant idea came to me as I cleared away the newspapers in the living room.

Pizza service! Why didn't I think of that in the first place? Mum probably wouldn't have anything against it. After all, today was my birthday, and she would be happy that I had friends round instead of spending the entire day in front of the TV like some **miserable wretch** watching depressing talk shows about loneliness.

Without a moment's hesitation I dialled the number of the pizza service and ordered ten family pizzas **à la maison**.

---

grim – düster;
ground almonds – gemahlene Mandeln;
miserable wretch – heulendes Elend;
à la maison – nach Art des Hauses

"Will it **fill** us **up**?" I asked. "I mean, we're really hungry."

The woman laughed. "Our family pizza has filled up everybody until now, but to be on the safe side you could order two more. You can always eat them cold or freeze them."

"OK," I said. "Then I'll take twelve pizzas, or make that fourteen. Then nothing can go wrong."

"Shall we bring any salad or dessert with that? And drinks?"

"No, thank you, that won't be necessary. I just need fourteen family pizzas as soon as possible. By six o'clock if that's OK?"

I wouldn't even mention the pizza service to my friends. I'd just **pretend** I was always prepared for a spontaneous party with twenty guests. I'd casually say, "Oh, that's **handy**, I've got a little something to eat in the kitchen!" or something like that. I'd seen that in a film and thought the scene was great.

By now it was time I got **changed** to suit the occasion. I decided to wear my old jeans and a white **lacy** T-shirt. I liked the combination a lot, because it didn't make me look overdressed. None of my guests would guess I was expecting them.

---

to fill up – satt machen;
to pretend – so tun als ob;
handy – praktisch;
to change – hier: sich umziehen; lacy – mit Spitzen

At twenty to six I suddenly realised I'd have to pay for the pizzas as well. The only problem was I'd given the last bit of cash to Tom for my fantastic mahogany dye. But Mum would probably forgive me if I borrowed something from her. After all, it was my birthday and to go for dinner would probably be just as expensive.

I grabbed the sugar bowl, which was where Mum usually kept her household money, and **froze**. Instead of finding the usual collection of loose change and banknotes, there was no more than a gaping void.

For a moment I thought I might have picked up the wrong sugar bowl, but as much as I **hunted through** the kitchen cupboard, I couldn't find a cent anywhere.

There was no point looking for money in Simon's room, I knew that already. But I still tried, and I happened to come across a magazine with suggestions for presents. Oh, so that's how Simon came up with the idea of the earrings! I quickly flicked through the magazine and marked a ridiculously expensive bag and a lacy silver top with a large cross. Satisfied with my selection, I put the magazine back down. That should help Simon buy my next Christmas present.

Then I called Mum.

---

to freeze – hier: erstarren;
to hunt through – durchsuchen

Mailbox, as before.

"Please call me back, I'm **in deep trouble**. Honest. It's really important. Please call within the next ten minutes." I hung up and called back half a minute later. "Otherwise there's going to be a disaster," I added.

Sometimes one just has to **resort** to such methods with my mum. I just hoped she would listen to her mailbox soon.

Minute after minute passed, but the telephone didn't ring. I had no other choice but to search the entire flat looking for money.

At first I **set about it** pretty unsystematically, but then I tried to put myself in the position of a burglar and thought: where would you normally hide money? But either Mum was a lot cleverer than any burglar, or we were broke, because I ended up finding absolutely nothing! NOTHING!

All I found were two old Deutschmark coins and a few Italian lire in a handbag on the wardrobe. Apart from that, nothing! It was enough to drive me to the **brink of despair**!

It was no good; I'd just have to cancel the order for the family pizzas and hope that no one would be hungry.

---

in deep trouble – in großen Schwierigkeiten;
to resort to sth – auf etwas zurückgreifen;
to set about sth – etwas angehen;
the brink of despair – der Rand der Verzweiflung

But for some reason it just wasn't my day.

"Cancel the order?" echoed the women, **horror-struck**. "You can't cancel the order. The pizzas are on their way. We sent the bicycle courier especially. It's the quickest way in this rush hour traffic. I thought it was really urgent."

"Yes," I said **feebly**. "It is really urgent." Then I hung up.

There wasn't any point calling Mum again, and Simon hadn't even taken his mobile phone with him; I'd seen it lying on his bed. I guess the battery was flat again.

For a moment I thought about whether I should try and **scrounge** some cash off the neighbour, but then I remembered that she'd complained about my loud music only a few days ago, and I decided, as always, to try and get through the situation as it was.

I mean, I was fourteen years old; I'd think of something. I tore the batik scarf off my head. I felt stupid walking around like that. Besides, it was far too hot for a headscarf. I'd just have to stand by my orange and red hairdo.

Just after six o'clock the doorbell rang.

There was nothing I could do but try to **negoti-**

---

horror-struck – voller Entsetzen;
feebly – schwach; to scrounge – sich leihen;
to negotiate – verhandeln

ate with the bicycle courier and offer him something as a **deposit**. My new earrings maybe? Or maybe I should **trade in** the TV? Or my CD player?

He rang again.

I took a deep breath and opened the front door.

"No!"

"I'm sorry?"

I stared at the boy in front of the door. Dark eyes, black curly hair – I took a deep sigh. I was **tempted** just to turn around and slam the door behind me!

This couldn't be happening to me!

But how was I **supposed to** know that David worked as a bicycle courier and – of all people – it would be him who would deliver my fourteen family pizzas, all neatly wrapped in red, green and white cardboard boxes?

I wanted to disappear into the next mouse hole. This was more than **embarrassing**: standing in front of me was the boy who I'd been thinking about practically every minute for the past three weeks and two days, and he was smiling at me really sweetly.

"I guess you're pretty hungry, right?"

"No, I just..." I stuttered. "Yeah, sure, that's why I ordered fourteen."

---

deposit – Pfand;
to trade in – etwas in Zahlung geben;
to be tempted – versucht sein;
to be supposed to – sollen;
embarrassing – peinlich

I laughed out loud for a second, and then I remembered my outrageous hairdo! Reddy orange! Just awful! Completely **whacky**! What was David going to think of me? I was behaving like a **panic-stricken** chicken.

With the last remains of **dignity** I pointed to the kitchen. "Over there, please," I mumbled, trying to wrap the batik scarf, which I'd thrown into the hallway corner, around my head as **inconspicuously** as possible.

But, of course, just then I had to get caught up in the hanging mobile – dancing swans made of **down feathers** – which Simon had hung up in the hall on Mum's birthday two months ago, with the result that I tore down the entire construction.

"Are you alright?" called David from the kitchen.

"Fine. Everything's fine," I mumbled, trying to get the feathers out of my hair.

"Shall I put the pizzas in the fridge…?

"No, wait!" I quickly called. I'd suddenly remembered that I'd been keeping my make-up in the fridge to protect it from the heatwave.

But it was too late. He'd already opened the fridge door and was staring **at a loss** at the carton

---

whacky – verrückt, daneben;
panic-stricken – aufgescheucht;
dignity – Würde; inconspicuously – unauffällig;
down feathers – Daunenfedern;
at a loss – ratlos

of milk, the jam jar and the twenty-five sorts of lipstick which I'd arranged according to their hue in the middle shelf. At the top of the fridge was my nail polish and eye shadow, but they were half hidden by a **lettuce**.

"No room left," he remarked.

Because I had the sneaking feeling that he wasn't into girls who wore lipstick, I lied about them all being product samples, and said that I personally thought so much colour in the face looked awful.

"Yeah," he just said as he put the pizza boxes down on the dining table.

I slipped a loose strand of reddy orange hair back under my blue headscarf and tried to put on a **beaming** smile. Something had to happen now. David was standing no more than two metres away from me; I just had to use the chance.

I felt myself breaking out into a sweat. Was that the situation or the summer heatwave?

Tiny beads of sweat were also shimmering on David's forehead. I couldn't take my eyes off him.

Through the open window I could hear the quiet laughter of children. Someone beeped their car horn. Then time seemed to stand still.

Just then his mobile phone rang, but it didn't seem to be important, because when he went to answer it, the caller had already hung up.

---

lettuce – Salat; beaming – strahlend

"Are you having a party?" asked David, pointing at the pizzas on the kitchen table. "Or do you really want to eat them all by yourself?"

I laughed nervously. I'd just had a crazy idea. Actually it was totally **insane**, but I didn't have any other choice. I had to try it.

"Yes, I'm having a party," I said, trying to maintain my smile. "It's my birthday today. I've turned fourteen."

"Congratulations," he said. "So? Have your wishes all come true?"

I closed my eyes for a moment. My biggest wish was possibly just about to come true. I just daren't **mess it up** now!

"I don't know yet," I mumbled.

The two of us fell silent.

David leaned against the kitchen table. He also seemed to be a bit nervous because he was toying with one of the pizza boxes.

The clock in the living room **chimed**. A quarter past six. In a quarter of an hour my birthday guests would start arriving.

"Right, then I hope you have a nice birthday," he said, looking at me. "By the way, is your foot still hurting? You remember? At the school party recently…? It really was an accident. Actually, it was

---

insane – wahnsinnig;
to mess it up – etwas vermasseln;
the clock chimed – die Uhr schlug

my **form teacher**'s fault. You see, he trod on my foot, and I took a step back, and..."

"Yes," I said, looking into his eyes. Dark brown eyes. Almost black.

I had to use all my strength to tear myself away. I saw a girl on the street who looked vaguely like a classmate of mine, and she dragged me back to reality. My guests would be arriving in a few minutes.

David **cleared his throat**. "I'll be off then. Oh, yes, I have to settle the bill first. Right, that comes to exactly..."

I took the bill out of his hand and put it down on the sideboard without even looking at it. "I'd really like to invite you to my party," I heard myself saying. It was completely **weird**, but my voice almost didn't **quiver** at all. "To my birthday party. Really, David, I'd really love it if you stayed and celebrated with me."

If he was surprised, then he didn't show it. He just smiled and said he'd really like to and it was a really great idea, but unfortunately...

"But unfortunately?" I asked. I **felt sick with fear**.

It was happening just as I feared it might. I'd fi-

---

form teacher – Klassenlehrer;
to clear one's throat – sich räuspern;
weird – schräg, seltsam;
to quiver – beben, zittern;
to feel sick with fear – einem ist schlecht vor Angst

nally managed to **pluck up the courage** and what happened? David turned me down! After his "but unfortunately" I couldn't expect anything else.

David pulled his mobile phone out of his pocket and stared at the display. That was it! His girlfriend had probably sent him an SMS: where had he got to?

I really wanted to cry! And the most embarrassing thing of all was still to come. I'd have to tell him that I didn't have a cent, and he'd have to take the fourteen family pizzas with him. I took a deep breath. I definitely would not cry!

"It's cool," I said. "It was just a question."

He hesitated for a moment. "I don't want to disappoint my friend. But if it's alright, I'll come around later. Is that OK?"

I nodded. Just be cool, I said to myself. Just pretend not to be particularly interested. "Whatever you want. If you can't make it, it's not the end of the world." I **chuckled**, but I thought it sounded really **fake**. "There are enough people coming." I took the bill off the sideboard. "I almost forgot to pay. 65 Euros! That's cheap."

David nodded. "There's a free pizza if you order ten or more."

I took the purse out of the table drawer and

---

to pluck up the courage – allen Mut zusammennehmen;
to chuckle – kichern;
fake – gekünstelt

opened it. Was I actually expecting a **miracle**? Probably, but miracles only happen in **fairy-tales**, and the purse was just as empty as it had been an hour ago.

"Whoops!" I pretended. "Strange! Where's the money? I thought my mum had left me enough money behind to..." I shook my head. "Do you know what I mean? I was quite sure that..."

"Maybe she used it to get some **petrol**," he said. "But it doesn't matter. I'm not going back to the pizzeria again today. I can leave the bill here, and you can pay there directly tomorrow. That's the easiest solution, don't you think?"

On the one hand I was really **relieved** that everything had gone so **smoothly**, but on the other hand... I'd probably never see David again – at the most **in passing** at school, or at the next school party.

I was about to say something, but David looked at his watch and said he had to go. His friend would be really angry if he came too late. Besides, he didn't know exactly where the party he was going to was taking place.

"OK then," I said. "You know the way out."

The mere fact that my birthday guests would be

---

miracle – Wunder; fairy-tales – Märchen;
petrol – Benzin; relieved – erleichtert;
smoothly – glatt;
in passing – im Vorbeigehen

arriving in five minutes at the latest, and that by then I'd have to take all the pizzas out of the boxes and get rid of the packing inconspicuously, was the only thing which stopped me from throwing myself onto my bed in tears.

I **piled up** the pizzas in the oven, turned the CD player with my favourite songs up to full volume and waited. I swore to myself I wouldn't think of David for the whole evening. At least that was the plan.

Something had probably gone wrong again, because it wasn't until half past seven that I heard some **commotion** on the street.

I tore open the front door.

"Happy birthday to you!" **yelled** my guests.

Half of my class had come, and there were a few others from school as well.

"And now we're going to sing a song for you!"

The neighbour threw open a window, but as the **mob** burst into a song in front of my front door, even Mrs Meulenberger smiled. She'd probably complain about the **racket** later.

"That's no reason to cry," said Jenny. "**Blimey**, Tanja, you should be happy."

---

to pile up – aufstapeln;
commotion – Spektakel;
to yell – schreien; mob – Pack; racket – Krach;
blimey – Mensch!

"I am happy," I sniffled. "Honest. I'm **over the moon**. This is such a..."

"...mega surprise!" called Lisa. "Tanja, admit it, you didn't see it coming. Henri called us, and we spent all afternoon calling around, and because we're invading your place like this, we brought something with us. Andreas, where are you?" She waved over to a boy who was pulling a **handcart**.

"Look under the towel. We brought it with us," said Sandra.

I cautiously lifted the **crocheted cloth** to one side. "No," I said. "No, I don't believe it."

"Great surprise, isn't it?" Jenny beamed at me. "We thought you probably wouldn't have anything to eat in the house when twenty people turned up all of a sudden, and Kathrin came up with the idea of buying some family pizzas. That's why we're a bit late. Someone had already bought up half the pizzeria, and we had to wait for ages. Can we put the pizzas in your oven and warm them up?"

I shook my head. "Unfortunately, the oven is broken," I lied. "But the idea with the pizzas is cool. Come in. It's great you're here."

"I think we bought too many pizzas," said Pascal, a boy from another class in the same year as me. "For

---

over the moon – überglücklich;
handcart – Bollerwagen;
crocheted cloth – Häkeldecke

some reason the number of pizzas is **increasing**, not getting smaller."

I just shrugged my shoulders and grinned a bit. There was no way he could know that I kept bringing new supplies from the kitchen. No one – really no one – would ever have guessed that Andreas (who was really nice, by the way) had **unwittingly** told me everything. I just had to keep playing the game.

For a teeny-weeny moment I allowed myself to think of David – it would have been so nice if he were here. And Henri, of course! I **got on well** with the others from my class, but it was different with Henri, closer.

Perhaps there really was something like telepathy, because right then the telephone rang. It was Henri!

I went off to my room so I could speak on the phone without being disturbed.

"So?"

I laughed. "This is a great surprise party, Henri! Thanks for organising it for me! **It's** just **a shame** you're not here. And Tom, of course. But everything's really just great! By the way, you wouldn't believe it, but Leila's trying to **chat up** Jossi."

---

to increase – ansteigen, anwachsen;
unwittingly – unwissentlich;
to get on well with sb – sich mit jmdm. gut verstehen;
it's a shame – es ist schade; to chat up – jmdn. anbaggern

"And how are you?"

For some reason I thought my friend's voice sounded strange. Maybe it was just down to the bad connection. It sounded like she was still on her way to Düsseldorf. I could hear her parents talking in the background. "I already said: I'm feeling fine."

"And… what about David?"

At first I wanted to tell her that he'd brought me the pizzas, but I remembered just in time that no one should know about that.

"What about him?" I asked, trying to sound as disinterested as possible. "I guess he's enjoying his holidays."

"That's not what I meant." Henri sounded really nervous. "I mean, is he…"

I laughed. "Henri, I've **put** the whole thing with David **behind me**. It's for the best. Really, being solo is a lot less complicated. Don't you remember the trouble Simon had with his girlfriend? I think he's over the moon that the whole thing's over."

"It doesn't matter," Henri **interrupted** me. "Listen, my battery is running low. I have to hang up."

The line went dead a few seconds later.

I heard the others laughing out loud in the living room. I should have been really happy, but… I had to think about David again.

---

to put sth behind oneself – sich etwas abschminken;
to interrupt – unterbrechen

Before I'd had time to get really sad, the phone rang again.

"I borrowed Anette's mobile," said Henri. "You know how **stingy** she is, so I have to keep the call short. Listen, I just realised I haven't given you your birthday present yet."

"You don't need to give me anything, Henri."

She laughed nervously. "Oh yes, I do. I hope you like it. I left it in the **playground** in Meisenweg. I hope you don't get me wrong. It's just because you're my very best friend."

"In the playground? But someone will steal it!"

"No, it's not what you think. You have to go over there as quickly as possible and pick it up. The present is right in front of the **swings**. I didn't wrap it up. Tanja, please, whatever happens, **take it in your stride**."

I was just about to say something when she hung up on me.

It looked like the heat had gone to Henri's head. She'd sounded so strange. Normally, Henri is really **sensible**, but just now she sounded a bit mad.

"There's something I have to do quickly," I said to Jenny and Ole, who were dancing close together in the hall.

---

stingy – knauserig;
playground – Spielplatz; swing – Schaukel;
to take sth in one's stride – mit etwas gut fertig werden;
sensible – vernünftig

Jenny nodded and mumbled something.

"If my mum and Simon come home, tell them I'll be back in a minute," I added.

Hopefully, Mum wouldn't be angry. She'd originally wanted to go and eat with me… and instead of that twenty people were having a party in our living room.

Andreas came out of the kitchen. "Did someone just ring the doorbell?" he asked. "I know some more people wanted to come."

"Then open the door if someone rings," I said. "I have **to pop out** quickly."

The air smelt of warm summer rain as I walked along Marien street. The sky was pitch-black in the west; it looked like a **storm** was **brewing**. I even thought I heard a slight **rumble**, but that might just have been the motorway.

How did Henri come up with the idea of leaving a present for me at the playground? It was probably some joke or something. Maybe Tom had put it there, and was now hiding in the bushes with a camera. Perhaps that was the surprise!

I decided to remain incredibly cool, whatever happened.

---

to pop out – nach draußen gehen;
storm – Gewitter;
to brew – sich zusammenbrauen;
rumble -- Grollen

When I turned into the small path to the playground, the first drops of rain began to fall. Everything had suddenly become really dark, but it was still light enough for me to see that someone was leaning against the swing. I **screwed up my eyes**. Yes, it could have been Tom.

I approached cautiously. Just then the figure turned around. We stared at each other.

"David? What are you doing here?"

Was David my present? I felt the rain falling onto my face and **mingling** with my tears.

"Tanja, there's no need to cry. Everything's fine," murmured David.

"I'm not crying," I sniffled, and I didn't really cry properly. I just had the feeling that something really big and important had just happened to me. And in situations like that I always have to cry, even in the cinema, too. I just can't help it.

David pulled me over to the pirate ship where we **took shelter** from the pouring rain. It seemed to be coming from all sides. A **gale** had started, and I was freezing cold in my thin blouse.

David put his denim jacket around my shoulders. "And what are you doing here at this time of night?" he asked.

---

to screw up the eyes – die Augen zusammenkneifen;
to mingle – sich vermischen;
to take shelter – Unterschlupf suchen;
gale – Sturm

"That's a long story," I mumbled and had to think of Henri, the best friend in the world. "It has something to do with my birthday."

He nodded. "Didn't you say you were having a party? Maybe…" he hesitated for a second, "if your invitation is still valid… maybe I could come, too?"

"Of course! But I thought you were going to a party…"

"I am, or was. It's really strange: I got this SMS telling me to wait here until the next SMS came, but **for some reason** it didn't seem to work. I've been waiting here for almost half an hour, and nothing's happened. Tom said he would …"

"Tom? Oh, right, Tom." I had to smile.

I just felt incredibly good. Henri and Tom, I thought, I'll never, ever forget this!

"Come on," I said, and all of a sudden everything was so easy. True, I had orange coloured hair, and yes, I am really **shy**, but now I just smiled at David, took him by the hand and ran home with him through the warm summer rain, where my friends and Simon and Mum were waiting for us.

---

for some reason – aus irgendeinem Grund;
shy – schüchtern

Ebenfalls auf Englisch bei Thienemann erschienen:

Sabine Both: *Move to Cloud Nine*
Christamaria Fiedler: *Spaghetti Crime*
Sissi Flegel: *Forbidden to Love*
Bianka Minte-König: *Mobile Phone Love*
Hortense Ullrich: *Never Kiss a Witch*
Zimmermann & Zimmermann: *Maths, Stress and a Lovesick Heart*

Summer, Sun & Holiday Love
Aus dem Deutschen von David Fermer
ISBN 3 522 17775 4

Reihengestaltung: Birgit Schössow
Einbandillustration: Birgit Schössow
Texttypografie: Marlis Killermann
Schrift: Meridien
Satz: KCS GmbH, Buchholz/Hamburg
Reproduktion: Medienfabrik, Möglingen
Druck und Bindung: Friedrich Pustet, Regensburg

5 4 3 2 1 * 05 06 07 08

Thienemann im Internet: www.thienemann.de